D0934678

HEALTH

in the

ELEMENTARY SCHOOL

The Role of the Classroom Teacher

By

HERBERT WALKER

PROFESSOR OF HEALTH EDUCATION
TEACHERS COLLEGE, COLUMBIA UNIVERSITY

THE RONALD PRESS COMPANY • NEW YORK

Library of Congress Catalog Card Number: 55-7723

PRINTED IN THE UNITED STATES OF AMERICA

To
V. D. W.

PREFACE

SUBSTANTIAL progress in the health care of children has been made during the past few decades—progress to which school health programs have contributed extensively. Nevertheless, much remains to be learned about the subject. Further advances will be made when more teachers and more school principals acquire a thorough understanding of the role of the classroom teacher in the school health program. No member of the elementary school staff is in a more strategic position than the classroom teacher for influencing the health welfare of school children. Through skillful guidance of projects that associate health problems with the daily living experiences of pupils, she can be influential in the development of desirable understanding and behavior. She can be instrumental in making programs of preventive and corrective work highly successful through her cooperation with health service specialists.

As opposed to books for nurses and specialists, and covering all grades, this book is written, primarily, for the elementary classroom teacher and for the college student who is preparing to teach in the elementary school. To be well prepared and able to carry on her work effectively, the teacher needs an understanding of educational principles as they apply in a health teaching program. She should be aware of the characteristics of a "normal healthy child," and she must recognize deviations from normal appearance and behavior when they exist. Because the school program is one aspect of the broad program of community health, the teacher also requires an elementary understanding, at least, of certain principles and practices of public health as they are applied in the elementary school health program. With such an understanding she is able not only to cooperate effectively with health specialists as they work in the elementary school, but also to relate the procedures she herself carries on in the classroom to the over-all program of community health.

In the following pages an attempt is made to present, in orderly fashion, the relationship of the work of the classroom teacher to these and to other aspects of a comprehensive school health program. The more technical aspects of public health as they apply in school health programs are not included. Oversimplification, however, is avoided.

Since many elementary school teachers do not have available the facilities and the personnel of organized school or public health departments and must rely on limited community health resources, suggestions are made for procedures which are desirable when the need arises for special health services for a child. The school administrator will also find suggestions which will be of help to him in establishing the place of school health in his plan for elementary education.

To the large number of elementary school teachers with whom he has worked in the field and to the students in his classes who have prepared for careers in elementary education, the writer is deeply indebted. Their practical and constructive suggestions and their genuine concern for the children in their care have been a source of help and inspiration.

HERBERT WALKER

Clinton, Connecticut
January, 1955

CONTENTS

HEALTH IN THE
ELEMENTARY SCHOOL

government has, among other responsibilities, legal responsibility for the control of communicable disease. In large and well-organized health departments, this control is a function of the bureau or the division of communicable diseases. In the small town or the small county, the health officer assumes direct responsibility for communicable disease control in addition to his other duties. The citizens of a community look to the chief medical officer and to the members of his staff for general leadership in all health work with children and adults.

The voluntary health agencies, which are supported by public contributions supplemented, in some instances, by endowment and which are concerned with specific health problems, such as tuberculosis or poliomyelitis, contribute extensively to the broad program of preventive and curative care for children. Frequently, special projects in public health, such as health education experiments which the department of health cannot assume because of budget limitations, are sponsored by voluntary health agencies. Because they sponsor such projects and because they are identified by the public with specific services in health, voluntary health agencies play an important role in the program of community health. In general, the work of these agencies supplements the activities of the department of health in providing a comprehensive health program for a community.

In the past, narrower concepts of the scope of public education did not include responsibilities which now are recognized as an essential part of the educational program. A broadening of the scope of public education has resulted from realization by parents and school officials that responsibilities of citizenship today call for an increasing identification of the individual with the affairs of his community. The health of an individual is no longer a concern only to himself. Because he helps to make the health statistics of the community in which he lives, the community shares concern for his health welfare. Although the primary purpose of the local board of education is to provide an educational program for children, this board has also a responsibility for the health of children attending school. There is evidence of this in state statutes and regulations adopted for the purpose by state and local boards of education.

The authority to manage and direct the health work in the public schools of the states has, for the most part, been vested in the local school districts under the supervision of state boards of health according to legislative enactments. Boards of education may, in turn, adopt rules and regulations to cover the specific needs of a given situation. These may include the adoption of rules to insure proper sanitation of school houses and school premises; the provision of health, nursing, and dental inspection of the pupils; the adoption of a program of physical education; and the reorganization of the curriculum to include subjects designed to promote a knowledge of the principles of healthful living.[1]

Further evidence of the responsibility of the school in child health work today is found in a report by Kilander which concerns financial and administrative responsibility for school health services in the United States (see Table 1).

A substantial part of this broad responsibility of the educational system for child health rests with the classroom teacher. She is in daily contact with each child during the school year, works cooperatively with child health specialists, and is a key person in relationships between the school and the home.

Need for Health Services

In the immediate future and in many parts of the United States, the agencies responsible for school health work must meet the need for a greater amount of service, because of expected increase in enrollment (see Fig. 1). This increasing

[1] Commission on Health in Schools, *Health in Schools*, Twentieth Yearbook of the American Association of School Administrators (1st ed.; Washington, D. C.: National Education Association, 1942), p. 324.

TABLE 1

AGENCIES RESPONSIBLE FOR FINANCING AND ADMINISTERING SCHOOL
HEALTH SERVICES IN CITIES OVER 2,500, BY CITY POPULATION
GROUP: 1950

City Population Group and Function 1	No. of Cities Reporting 2	Per Cent of School Health Services Under:			
		Board of Education 3	Board of Health 4	Joint Authority 5	Other Authority 6
United States	2,886				
Financing	———	54.9	10.5	23.3	11.3
Administering	———	60.2	10.9	23.0	5.9
Group I (100,000 and above)	93				
Financing	———	60.2	16.1	19.4	4.3
Administering	———	61.3	12.9	22.6	3.2
Group II (30,000 to 99,999)	251				
Financing	———	63.3	13.5	19.6	3.6
Administering	———	66.1	13.9	18.7	1.3
Group III (10,000 to 29,999)	668				
Financing	———	61.1	7.8	22.3	8.8
Administering	———	66.0	8.1	22.2	3.7
Group IV (2,500 to 9,999)	1,874				
Financing	———	51.2	10.8	24.4	13.6
Administering	———	57.3	11.4	24.0	7.3

SOURCE: Holger F. Kilander, "Health Services in City Schools—Administrative Aspects," *American Journal of Public Health*, XLIII (1953), 316. Percentages for 1940, which are given in Kilander's table, are omitted.

enrollment, already evident, reflects a larger school-age population and results also from required school attendance to at least sixteen years of age (seventeen or eighteen in some states), better enforcement of compulsory school attendance laws, and parental desire for increased educational opportunity for their children. Between 1950 and 1960 this increase in enrollment at the elementary school level will be about five million, but will not be uniformly distributed throughout the country. Marked differences in the present concentration of child population are shown in the extreme

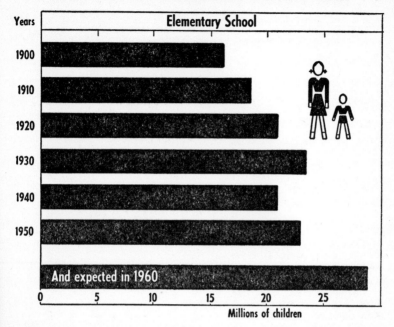

FIGURE 1. An Increase in Elementary School Enrollment Is Expected. Source: Midcentury White House Conference on Children and Youth, *Children and Youth at the Midcentury: A Chart Book* (Raleigh, N. C.: Health Publications Institute, Inc., 1951), Chart 67. Only the part of chart which applies to elementary school children is used.

examples of 158 children per square mile in Rhode Island and 0.3 in Nevada.[2] There is little reason to believe that the expected increase in school population will result in a more uniform distribution of pupils than exists at present.

In some localities a greatly enlarged school population will bring with it a highly organized and comprehensive school health program. However, in many parts of the country, the well-staffed school health department is not possible and will not be possible in the immediate future. The small school system, and in many cases, the one-room school will

[2] American Academy of Pediatrics, Committee for the Study of Child Health Services, *Child Health Services and Pediatric Education* (New York: Commonwealth Fund, 1949), p. 12.

continue to exist for some time to come.[3] This situation will place substantial responsibility on the classroom teacher for the health guidance of the elementary school child. In the smaller school systems she will necessarily assume, in addition to the usual child health care activities, many of the activities carried on by the school nurse and other health specialists found in the larger urban school systems.

When compared with the child of the early part of the century, the school child of today has marked advantages in reference to freedom from illness and from remediable defects. Enormous strides were made in the preventive and curative care of children during the fifty-year period between 1900 and 1950. Under mortality conditions prevailing at the beginning of the present century, 228 of 1,000 newborn infants failed to reach their twentieth birthday. Under present conditions, 50 of 1,000 newborn infants die before reaching twenty years of age (see Fig. 2).

Many factors were influential in bringing about this marked reduction in mortality. Immunizing procedures, the use of new chemical and biological preparations, better medical and nursing care, greater availability of medical care, and better sanitation were the foundation of this advance. In addition, a wider knowledge of child health care on the part of parents, more comprehensive programs of maternal and child health by public health and voluntary health agencies, and an extension of the responsibility of the school for child health all contributed to the health welfare of children.

In the earlier years of the twentieth century, as shown in mortality tables, diphtheria and typhoid fever were common disabling illnesses of children and often reached epidemic proportions. Advances in the techniques of immunization

[3] Midcentury White House Conference on Children and Youth, *Children and Youth at the Midcentury: A Chart Book* (Raleigh, N. C.: Health Publications Institute, Inc., 1951), Chart 72 and opposite.

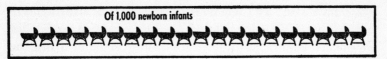

Of 1,000 newborn infants

Under mortality conditions at the beginning of the century

772

children would live to reach their 20th birthday

Under present mortality conditions

950

children would live to reach their 20th birthday

FIGURE 2. Chances of Children Surviving to Adulthood Are Greater Than Ever. Source: Midcentury White House Conference on Children and Youth, *Children and Youth at the Midcentury: A Chart Book* (Raleigh, N. C.: Health Publications Institute, Inc., 1951), Chart 37.

and in the better control of water and food supplies by public health agencies have now made possible practically complete freedom from these two diseases.

Challenge in Problems of Today

But despite the progress which has been made in child health, there is no room for complacency. Although problems in the health welfare of children are different from those of fifty years ago, they are still a definite challenge to education and to public health. Diphtheria and typhoid fever are no longer serious problems of childhood, but scarlet fever, measles, pneumonia, influenza, rheumatic fever, and poliomyelitis are serious problems in the health care of children. In addition to the more serious illnesses that result in varying percentages of fatality, there are the relatively minor but annoying disturbances that make life miserable for the child while they last. The common cold, digestive disturbances, and skin infections, for example, are the cause of many lost days of schooling. In these minor health problems which interfere with the child's living routine exists a challenge for child health work. In the main this challenge lies in the attempt to bridge the gap between our knowledge of healthful living, on the one hand, and the application of that knowledge, on the other. A contribution toward the solution of this problem lies in education designed to improve personal health behavior.

A report of the American Academy of Pediatrics sets forth four essential factors as the reasons why a large number of children do not receive preventive and curative care compatible with present standards of good pediatric practice: (1) parents are unable to pay for good services, (2) there is unwillingness to use, or lack of knowledge of, available facilities, (3) services are not available where many children live, and (4) there are not enough physicians well trained in the medical care and health supervision of children, especially in rural areas.[4]

The public school administrator and his staff cannot play a particularly significant role in influencing factors (1), (3), and (4) above, but factor (2) constitutes an opportunity to administrator, school teacher, and nurse who have a broad concept of health in the elementary school.

SELECTED REFERENCES

AMERICAN ACADEMY OF PEDIATRICS, Committee for the Study of Child Health Services. *Child Health Services and Pediatric Education.* New York: Commonwealth Fund, 1949.

BAIN, KATHERINE, and STUART, HAROLD C. "Facts and Figures about Child Health in the United States," *American Journal of Public Health,* XXXIX (September, 1949), 1091-98.

[4] American Academy of Pediatrics, Committee for the Study of Child Health Services, *op. cit.,* p. xiii.

COMMISSION ON HEALTH IN SCHOOLS. *Health in Schools,* rev. ed. Twentieth Yearbook of the American Association of School Administrators. Washington, D. C.: National Education Association, 1951.

METROPOLITAN LIFE INSURANCE CO. *The School Child—Health Progress and Needs.* New York: The Company, 1947.

MIDCENTURY WHITE HOUSE CONFERENCE ON CHILDREN AND YOUTH. *Children and Youth at the Midcentury: A Chart Book.* Raleigh, N. C.: Health Publications Institute, Inc., 1951.

SCHNEIDER, ELSA, and McNEELY, SIMON A. *Teachers Contribute to Child Health.* (Publication of the U. S. Office of Education, Bulletin No. 8.) Washington, D. C.: Government Printing Office, 1951.

WILSON, CHARLES C. (ed.). *Health Education,* 4th ed. National Education Association and American Medical Association, Joint Committee on Health Problems in Education. Washington, D. C.: National Education Association, 1948.

Chapter 2

THE MEASUREMENT OF PHYSICAL
GROWTH AND DEVELOPMENT

Unless deterred by disease, lack of adequate food, or other adverse influence, physical growth in school children continues in a more or less uniform pattern through the elementary school years. As each child proceeds toward maturity, he develops the characteristic size and shape which inheritance has predetermined for him, unless he is prevented from doing so by disturbing experiences which interfere with his pattern of growth.

Early investigations in the field of growth and development of children were concerned with establishing norms or standards of weight for chronological age and height. The relationship of a child's weight to the established weight norm for his age and height classified him as *normal, overweight,* or *underweight.* This classifying procedure was expected to become useful as a technique for determining an index of general health for an individual child. His health status was determined in the main by the extent to which he achieved the norm of weight for his chronological age and height. More recently, however, recognition of individual variation in the growth potential of children has resulted in discontinuing the use of norms of weight based on chronological age and height as a method of determining the index of general health status.

Individual Variation

Variation in the growth of individual children is due to several factors. The child inherits certain predispositions to body type and size as a result of the family from which he comes. The family may express, to some extent, its dominant racial origin, but casual observation shows such a wide individual variation within racial groups that a so-called *racial* tendency toward a body type may have little significance for a single individual. In attempts to construct present standards of growth, these factors have been taken into consideration by classifying individuals as *slender, medium,* or *stocky* types. However, classification of children on this basis has not proved to be a satisfactory procedure because of the difficulty in borderline cases of determining to which type the child actually belongs.

The inherited growth potential of a child determines the pattern of body build possible under ideal environmental conditions. These conditions, however, are not uniformly available for all growing children; for example, in experiences with childhood communicable diseases, and with conditions where there is disfunctioning of glands of internal secretion, which interferes with growth. Other influences, such as inadequate nutrition, chronic fatigue, and disturbing emotional situations, may also affect adversely the growth pattern of a child.

These various influences on growth and development may result in marked variation from normal size and shape. To illustrate, in cases of disfunctioning of the thyroid gland, in which there is extreme deficiency of thyroid secretion in early life, cretinism develops: the result is an improperly proportioned human being of inferior mental development. In other more common instances in which the child is continually disturbed emotionally, there may be interference with the normal digestive processes to the point of causing deficient tissue formation, and the child may be excessively lean.

We should be aware that each child is endowed with certain potentials of growth and development that are peculiar to him. He may not approach or may go beyond the average for his group. This is not important. Our concern should be that the child realize his own potentials just as nearly as possible.

School Procedures in Assessment

Among other specific responsibilities of schools in caring for the physical welfare of children is that of attempting to determine whether a child is proceeding toward maturity at the rate he should and in the way he should. That is, does the child show that he is growing and developing in such a way that he is meeting his own potential? The procedure of weighing and measuring, which gives a reasonably good indication of this, is not very complicated.

Classroom Weighing and Measuring

Weighing and measuring children is a fairly well-established procedure in the elementary school. The common practice in many schools is to weigh each child every month and to measure height two or three times a year. The classroom teacher can quite easily make routine determination of changes in the height and weight of her children. The equipment recommended is a device for measuring height, and a beam scales. For measuring height, either a yardstick attached to the wall or a reproduction of a yardstick marked off directly on the wall is satisfactory. The reproduction needs to include only the range of heights to be measured.

The immediate purpose of weighing and measuring is to determine the status of the child at the time and to find out how much progress he has made since the previous measurements. The normal child shows at least some increase in weight during a two-month period. Failure to gain for three successive months is adequate reason for the teacher to refer the child to the school nurse or physician for attention. If such service is not available, she may notify parents of their child's failure to gain in weight and may suggest that they obtain medical opinion about the child.

This screening of children for referral to school or private physician for careful examination is based on the concept that physical measurements, if properly interpreted, can be useful in helping to establish an index of the child's health. A normal healthy young animal grows. If there is failure to gain weight over a three-month period, this is usually an indication that there is an inadequacy in his food intake, a disturbing factor in his school or home environment, or a need for medical attention. His failure to show progress in growth is a reflection of a disturbing condition in his daily living.

Particular emphasis is placed on the fact that recordings of height and weight are not in themselves particularly significant. They are useful in adding to what is already known about the child. However, an interpretation of these measurements is not in the province of the classroom teacher. The interpretation of periodic measurements is the responsibility of the physician and is made in the light of other information about the child.

Recognition of the fact that each child has his own potential of growth and that our practical concern is to make sure he has the opportunity to realize his own inborn potential suggests we use the type of examining instrument which makes provision for individual variation. As has already been stated, we cannot expect satisfactory results through a comparison of the individual with weight norms based on age and height only.

Body Measurements

Recommendations by Stuart and Meredith about the use of body measurements of children in the school health program are of interest to teachers.[1] These investigators recommend taking measurements that reveal "over-all body size in length and mass and the relative amounts of the three principal body tissues which determine total mass, i.e., stockiness of the bony skeleton, bulkiness of the musculature, and quantity of skin and subcutaneous tissues."[2] The actual measurements taken are weight, height, hip width, chest circumference, and leg girth. Determination is also made of subcutaneous tissue.

The authors have prepared a cumulative record form on which the measurements can be recorded and which, when used in conjunction with recommended tables arranged by sex and age, indicates the individual's percentile position for each measurement. Evident also from an inspection of the form are the interrelationships between all the measurements and an indication of change, if any has occurred, in the individual's percentile position as he has grown older.

Stuart and Meredith give an example of the value of such measurements:

A boy age 6 years is found to weigh 43 lbs. This means little unless one knows that about 80 per cent of boys age 6 years weigh more than 43 lbs. It means more if one knows that this boy is not short and not of slender build, being up to the average for boys of 6 years in height, chest circumference, and hip width. It means still more if one knows that he weighed 41 lbs. at 5 years, which was nearly up to average, about 60 per cent weighing more than 41 lbs. at that age. Clearly this failure to gain normally is revealed and its extent recognized by bringing into juxtaposition the rankings of this boy at the two ages.[3]

[1] Harold C. Stuart and Howard V. Meredith, "Use of Body Measurements in the School Health Program," *American Journal of Public Health*, XXXVI (1946), 1365-86.

[2] *Ibid.*, p. 1367.

[3] *Ibid.*, p. 1376.

The measurements called for in the technique recommended by Stuart and Meredith may be made by a nurse or by an assistant who has received instruction; they serve as aids to the physician in his appraisal of the child.

Wetzel Grid

Wetzel has developed a form which is designed for recording progressive changes in growth and is referred to as the Wetzel Grid. Through the use of this Grid (see Fig. 3), children may be screened and then classified into one of two main groups:

1. Those who require intensive study because they have failed or are failing in growth and development, and
2. Those for whom suitable 'quick inspection' may be planned in order to locate possible minor physical defects.[4]

The practical application of the technique in a classroom situation is described by Scramlin:

Failure to gain weight, and excessive gain have always been just cause for concern, but we have been without adequate materials to assist us in evaluating the progress of children who have continued to increase in weight. How satisfactory was such progress? When does gain cease to be adequate for a given child and when does it become excessive? We have recognized that A, who is the tall slender type, could not be expected to progress identically with B, who is the same age but of the short stocky type. The height-weight-age tables have been of some assistance when based on body types but their limitations are too evident. Children's types are far more numerous than those provided for in such tables.

Certain technical systems of judging children, such as the ACH Index, perished because the use of them required specially trained personnel. We have urgently needed a system of judging the physical status and progress of children that was free from any personal judgment, that could be used by persons of average skill, and that was based on measurements which could be taken in any doctor's office, school, or home.

[4] Norman C. Wetzel, M.D., "The Simultaneous Screening and Assessment of School Children," *Journal of Health and Physical Education*, XIII (1942), 577.

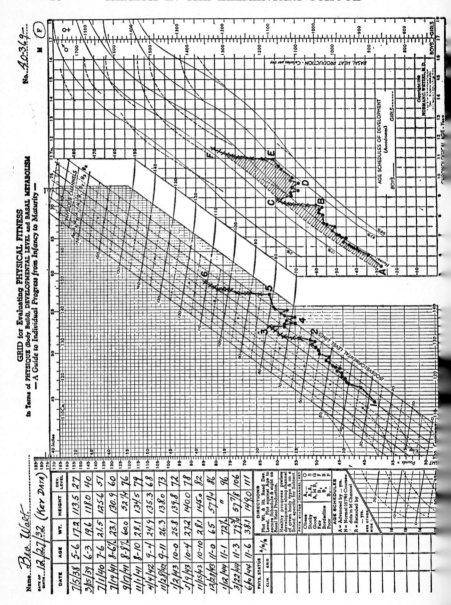

GRID for Evaluating PHYSICAL FITNESS
in Terms of PHYSIQUE (Body Build), DEVELOPMENTAL LEVEL and BASAL METABOLISM
— A Guide to Individual Progress from Infancy to Maturity —

Name: Bee West
Date: 12/27/32 (Key Data)
No. A 0369

DATE	AGE	WT.	HEIGHT	DEV. LEVEL
7/5/38	5-6	17.2	113.5	27
3/15/39	6-3	19.6	118.0	40
7/19/40	7-6	21.5	125.6	51
7/19/41	8-6¼	23.1	130.9	60
9/12/41	8-9½	60.0	52¼	76
11/14/41	8-10	28.1	134.5	79
4/4/42	9-1	24.9	135.3	68
11/28/42	9-11	26.3	138.0	73
12/14/43	10-0	25.8	139.8	72
7/9/43	10-4	27.2	140.0	78
11/5/43	10-10	28.1	145.0	82
12/20/43	11-0	65	57¼	86
1/24/44	11-1	73½	"	96
3/22/44	11-3	71¾	57⅞	106
6/6/44	11-6	38.1	147.0	111

(See notes on opposite page)

←——————————————————————————————————

Figure 3. Grid for Evaluating Physical Fitness. Source: Norman C. Wetzel, M.D., "The Role of the Grid Technique in a Physical Fitness Program," *Medical Woman's Journal* (November, 1948).

NOTES

A grid record showing two episodes of Simple Growth Failure (Malnutritional Type) plotted from the data tabulated in Metric or in English measures.

CHANNEL COURSE—Segments (1-2) and (3-4-5) represent moderate and severe departures from true channel-wise direction (1-3-6) with corresponding losses of physique from the B_1 B_2 body type first observed at (1). Segments (2-3) and (5-6) are recovery responses following treatment initiated at (2) and (5), physique having been completely restored at (3) and (6).

AUXODROMIC PROGRESS—As segment *(A-B)* deviates more and more from "own" or "expected" auxodrome *(ACF)*, speed of development is slowing down to values less than 1.0 level/month. Vertical difference between *ACF* and actual auxodrome *(ABCDEF)* measures *lag*, which amounts at *B* to 17 levels and at *E* to 22 levels. Segments *(B-C)* and *(E-F)* show speed-up during first and second recovery phases with complete return to own schedule at *C* and *F*. Failure in both episodes continued to increase until definite action had been taken at *(2,B)* and *(5,E)* to investigate causes and to remedy them.

FUEL-DEBT AREAS—*ABC:* 88,000 Calories; *CDEF:* 120,000 Calories.

REMARKS—By thus displaying when, and to what extent an individual child's growth is, or is not satisfactory, the Grid performs the function of a control chart: *(a)* Raw data are transformed into concrete terms, *viz.* body *size* (level) and *shape* (channel), and into *direction* and *speed* of development; *(b)* Individual progress is appraised with reference to a channel and an auxodrome specific to the subject; *(c)* Even slightly abnormal departures are easily distinguished from normal variations in direction and speed; *(d)* Tendency of trends to persist until conditions are changed affords a reliable basis for forecasts: unfavorable progress, in particular, tends definitely to become worse; *(e)* Close follow-up with repeated observations unmistakably verifies the influence of changed conditions during failure and recovery; *(f)* Results are objective and plainly visualized in contrast to "guess-work" of attempting "to interpret" height-weight data by mere inspection, or even by comparison with meaningless age-averages of various kinds; *(g)* Pupil-classification is simplified and put on the basis of individual need, whereas action and co-operative effort on the part of parents, teachers, physical educators, nurses, physicians and others is encouraged through common understanding of whether growth has failed or succeeded in operating satisfactorily.

We believe this problem has come a long way toward solution in the Grid for Evaluating Physical Fitness as developed by Dr. Norman C. Wetzel. The fundamentals of the Grid are so logical one wonders that it was not developed earlier. Only an intimate working acquaintance with it gives one an appreciation of the time and labor involved in the final product, or its simplicity and value in practical work.

A Grid record is composed of two graphs and uses no more complex data than height, weight, and age of the child, which have always been the routine figures collected for the basic estimate of the child's physical status. . . .

The left side of the Grid, on which the height and weight are plotted, is traversed by seven diagonal channels. These channels represent various body types. A child whose graph travels in one of the two channels at the extreme left will be classified as stocky and one whose graph falls outside the panel to the left is obese. The center channels A-1, M, and B-1, are rated "good." Although there may be some small-boned children whose natural graphs will follow channels B-2 or even B-3, the author of the Grid feels that these children should be screened for very careful watching and follow-up. Nutritionally they are classified as fair and borderline. A child whose graph falls outside the panel to the right is rated nutritionally as poor.

Any given height and weight of the child plotted on the Grid will determine his physical status and body build at that time. Only a series of heights and weights so plotted will determine whether or not his progress is satisfactory. Under normal conditions a child's channel will not be determined until the sixth or seventh year as the body types of small children undergo considerable change as they develop. A healthy child whose graph begins to leave its channel and deviate to the left, after his channel has been determined, should be watched for beginning obesity. Similarly, if a child's graph drops out of its channel to the right the beginning of malnutrition is indicated and the child and his environment should be checked for all the causes which may be contributing factors.

Healthy development not only prefers channelwise progress but should also proceed at a rate of approximately a point (or level) a month. This is measured by the parallel lines in black which cut diagonally across the lines and is known as his developmental level.

The panel on the right of the Grid, on which the second graph is made, uses ages for the horizontal axis and development levels for the vertical axis. Traversing diagonally across this panel are five curves called "auxodromes" which represent the various schedules according to which children progress toward maturity. The months or years a child is accelerated or retarded are measured from the center one of these standard auxodromes. It is not always obvious that even healthy normal children of the same age may vary widely in their physical development. One boy of twelve years may be inches taller and pounds heavier than another of the same age yet both may be progressing normally. One is merely approaching maturity on an earlier schedule than the other.

Failure of the child's graph to parallel one of these curves should also be a cause for concern. A comprehensive picture of the child's growth and development is obtained from the two graphs. Such an estimate has the distinct advantage of being free from any personal element. The influences of the child's hygiene, responsiveness, economic status, social adjustment, etc., are often difficult factors to rule out in the usual subjective judgment of his physical condition.[5]

Physical Growth Record

Meredith has developed growth record charts designed to supply "interesting and helpful information regarding the physical growth of school children."[6] "The charts . . . were constructed using percentile values obtained on a sample of the elementary and high school population. Specifically, the values used were the 1st, 10th, 30th, 70th, 90th, and 99th percentiles for height and weight at each successive annual age from 4 to 18. These six percentiles for each age and measurement were regarded as delimiting five zones."[7] Only two measurements, height and weight, are necessary for making out the record form. On the basis of these two measurements, the individual's growth may be plotted.

The growth record charts prepared by Meredith have been utilized by the Joint Committee on Health Problems

[5] E. Nancy Scramlin, "The Grid Method of Assessing Children," *Hoosier Health Herald*, XXVII (1946), 83-85.

[6] Howard V. Meredith, "A Physical Growth Record for Use in Elementary and High Schools," *American Journal of Public Health*, XXXIX (1949), 878.

[7] *Ibid.*, p. 883. The sample was composed of children who (1) were of northwest European ancestry (90 per cent), while only a scattering were of southeast European descent, and (2) were living under better-than-average conditions.

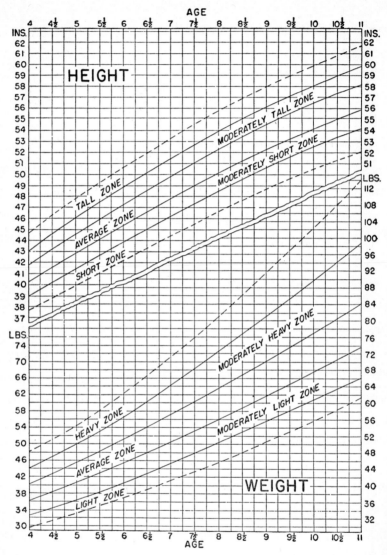

FIGURE 4. Physical Growth Record for Boys

Source for Figures 4 and 5: Joint Committee on Health Problems in Education of the National Education Association and the American Medical Association, *Health Education,* ed. Charles C. Wilson, M.D. (4th ed., 1948,

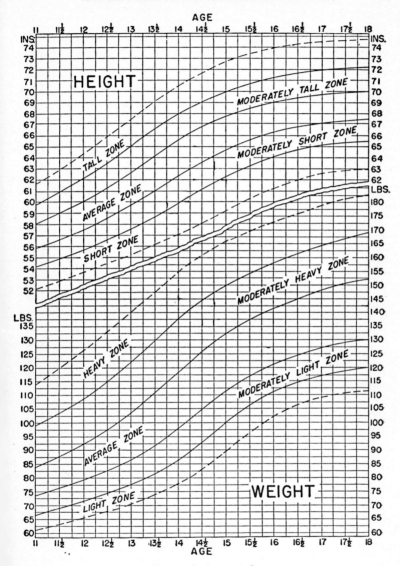

FIGURE 4—*Continued*

pp. 10-13), using data prepared by Howard V. Meredith, *Physical Growth Record for Boys—Girls* (Chicago: American Medical Association, and Washington, D. C.: National Education Association).

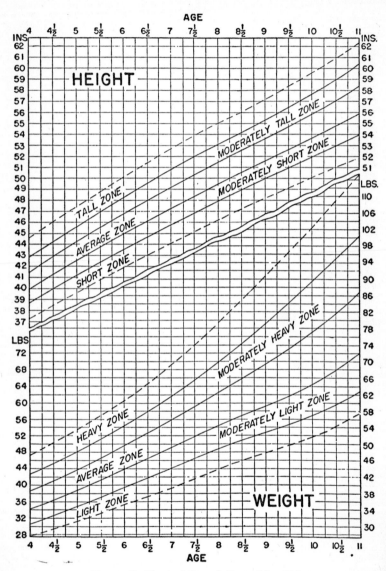

FIGURE 5. Physical Growth Record for Girls

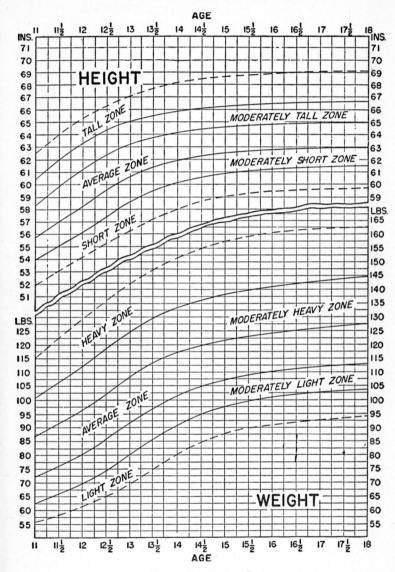

FIGURE 5—*Continued*

in Education of the National Education Association and the American Medical Association to prepare physical growth record forms for boys and girls (see Figs. 4 and 5). Repeated plotting of measurements shows a curve of progress in growth. Inspection of the record form reveals the individual's standing as related to others in the same chronological age group. A difference in the zone in which the two measurements of an individual fall (for example, height in the moderately tall zone and weight in the moderately light zone) suggests that he should be referred for a clinical opinion. He may be a healthy individual of slender build, or he may have a nutritional disturbance that interferes with his meeting his growth potential.

Value of Assessment for Health Guidance

The practice of recording measurements of the physical growth of children is one of the most useful techniques in health guidance. By making measurements, the teacher can become better informed about the physical characteristics of her pupils. In event of a change in the pattern of physical growth, she has a sound basis for referring the child to the health specialist—the nurse, or the school or private physician.

Routine measurements of children may also be used by the teacher as a sound motivating device in health teaching. The relationship between good eating habits (as indicated by choosing the proper kinds and amounts of food, for example) and the child's progress in physical growth can be made clear in a very direct way. Other habits which involve personal hygiene, such as getting adequate sleep and rest and avoiding respiratory infection (which as a chronic condition can interfere with good nutritional status), can be related to the individual's pattern of growth.

There is, in addition, an opportunity for the classroom teacher to utilize the child's record of growth as a report of progress to his parents. Such a report can be instrumental in building up between school and home a working relationship which promotes a more effective total health guidance program. Cooperative activity, established as a result of home and school interest in the pattern of the child's physical growth, can include attention to other aspects of child care, such as communicable disease control and the correction of remediable defects.

SELECTED REFERENCES

BRECKENRIDGE, MARIAN E., and VINCENT, E. LEE. *Child Development; Physical and Psychological Growth through the Years*, 2d ed. Philadelphia: W. B. Saunders Co., 1949.

GESELL, ARNOLD L. *The Child from Five to Ten*. New York: Harper & Bros., 1946.

JENESS, RACHEL M., and SOUTHER, SUSAN P. *Methods of Assessing the Physical Fitness of Children*. (Publication of the U. S. Children's Bureau, No. 263.) Washington, D. C.: Government Printing Office, 1940.

MEREDITH, HOWARD V. "A Physical Growth Record for Use in Elementary and High Schools," *American Journal of Public Health*, XXXIX (July, 1949), 878-85.

STUART, HAROLD C., and MEREDITH, HOWARD V. "Use of Body Measurements in the School Health Program," *American Journal of Public Health*, XXXVI (December, 1946), 1365-86; XXXVII (November, 1947), 1435-38.

WETZEL, NORMAN C. "Assessing the Physical Condition of Children," *Journal of Pediatrics*, XXII (January, 1943), 82-110; (February, 1943), 208-25; (March, 1943), 329-61.

————. *The Treatment of Growth Failure in Children*. Cleveland, Ohio: NEA Service, Inc., 1948.

Chapter 3

PROCEDURES IN HEALTH GUIDANCE

THE HEALTH guidance program of the elementary school consists mainly of (1) procedures for maintaining health through the prevention of disease and dysfunction and for correcting remediable defects, and (2) procedures for bringing about cooperation among home, school, and community in child health work.

Health Appraisal

Basic to all procedures of prevention and correction is careful and adequate appraisal of the individual child. Periodic health appraisal has taken the place of an inspectional type of program which was formerly used. Though not now in common use, *medical inspection* and *physical examination* were the terms used to describe this program. As time went on and health work with children became firmly established as a responsibility of education, a more comprehensive purpose developed in connection with the work of physicians in schools. This work, intended originally to supplement the efforts of the official health agencies to control childhood communicable diseases, is now a broadly conceived program of health guidance by school physicians, nurses, and dentists. Communicable disease control today is only one part of this program. The scope of health guidance in a well-organized school health program is seen in the close working relationships that exist within the school system with such departments as guidance, instruction, social service, pupil accounting, physical education, and building and grounds. In addition to responsibility for all aspects of the immediate physical welfare of children, the more comprehensively organized school health departments include responsibility for such programs as psychological and psychiatric services and health welfare of board of education employees.

Duties of Health Specialists

The scope of present-day services to schools by physicians and nurses is evident in official statements of the professional qualifications of physicians and nurses for school health work. The Committee on Professional Education of the American Public Health Association in its revised report recognizes the broad nature of the school physician's responsibilities:

Although not responsible for medical care of individual children, his successful contribution to the school health program necessitates that he have an understanding of:

1. The growth and development of children.
2. Diseases of children, and particularly, the health and accident hazards important to children of school age.
3. The values, methods, and limitations of advisory service to parents, teachers, school administrators, and pupils concerning the promotion of optimum growth and development.
4. The over-all school program and the types of adjustment which are possible and necessary for some children because of health reasons.
5. Methods of integrating school health services with health education, physical education, recreation, special education, lunchroom services, and other aspects of school life.
6. The treatment facilities of various types available in the community.
7. Technics of counseling with parents, pupils, and teachers concerning health problems, methods for their follow-up, and ways of solving them.

8. Individual and community health problems which may be attacked through education.
9. The place of the school as an important center for improving the health of a community.
10. The effect of environmental factors, physical and emotional, on the health, safety, and growth of pupils.
11. The effect of working conditions, physical and emotional, on the health and attitudes of teachers, and thus indirectly on pupils.
12. Principles and technics of group relations and group work, since the school health program must be a cooperative enterprise if it is to be successful.[1]

The National Conference for Cooperation in Health Education has reported in detail on the responsibilities of the nurse working in schools.[2] Some of these responsibilities are summarized in the statement which follows:

The nurse—
1. In the school health services program
   a) Makes all arrangements for the health examination of school pupils and of school personnel.
   b) Interprets the findings of the medical examination to parents and assists in follow-up of the recommendations which are made by the physician.
   c) Assists in identifying handicapped children and in arranging modifications in their school program.
   d) Assists teachers in the acquisition of competencies necessary for determining the health status of children in the classroom.
   e) Assumes a responsible role in the control of communicable disease.
   f) Gives active assistance in caring for accidents and sudden illness.
2. In the control of environment
   a) Knows the sanitary regulations which apply to the school plant.

[1] "Proposed Report on Educational Qualifications of School Physicians," *American Journal of Public Health*, XLIII (1953), 75.
[2] National Conference for Cooperation in Health Education, *The School Administrator, Physician, and Nurse in the School Health Program* (New York: Metropolitan Life Insurance Co., 1945), pp. 24-27.

b) Aids the administrator and the teacher in planning the school day so that the health needs of teachers and pupils are met.

c) Assists in periodic appraisal of the school plant and the school health program.

3. In health education

a) Helps the physician to make the health examination an educational experience for the child and the parent.

b) Assists the teacher in curriculum planning for health instruction and in the teaching of special topics, such as first aid and home nursing.

4. In home and community relationships

a) Aids in developing cooperative relationships between the schools and the official health agency and the voluntary agencies.

b) Interprets the school health program to the home and to others in the community.

c) Represents the school in relationships with community agencies when services are required for a child.

Responsibility for Services

One of the problems that arose during the extension of health guidance in the schools was to determine whether the work done by physician, nurse, dentist, and other specialists should be a function of the board of education or of the board of health. Arguments for both sides of the question have been presented.

The Joint Committee on Health Problems in Education of the American Medical Association and the National Education Association summarizes some of the advantages and disadvantages presented by advocates of the two different points of view:

A. The arguments in favor of administration exclusively by schools are:

1. All health services can more readily be made educational in character.

2. The director understands educational aspects of health service better than a nonschool official.

3. Better coordination with all educational phases of the school program is possible.
4. Better administrative control is possible—all school health activities can be under one responsible head.
5. More intensively trained and educationally oriented personnel may be employed.
6. Health personnel can concentrate on problems of school children.

B. The arguments in favor of health services administered by health department are:
1. The health department is legally responsible for control of communicable diseases.
2. School services, especially nursing, can be better coordinated into the generalized public health nursing program.
3. Generalized community nurses may have better home contacts than nurses working exclusively in schools.
4. Medical services should be under medical supervision.
5. All private schools must be serviced by the health department and duplicate organizations are wasteful.[3]

As the above statements indicate, certain aspects of the school health program require the technical skills of a medically trained person normally employed by the official health agency. In addition, legal authority for the community control of communicable disease is a function of the official health agency. In reference to these practical aspects of school health work, the official health agency can be more effective than the board of education in obtaining specific end-results.

The primary purpose for the existence of the services of health specialists in schools is the welfare of the individual child. Discussion about prerogatives sometimes loses sight of this fact. Clearly, the problem calls for cooperative effort between the official health agency and the board of education. One of the more important criteria for determining which department assumes responsibility for specific activi-

[3] *Health Education* (4th ed.; Washington, D. C.: National Education Association, 1948), pp. 98, 101.

ties lies in the answer to the question: Which department can be most effective in the solution of the health problem of the individual child? However, in most situations today, cooperation between boards of health and boards of education is no longer a problem.

Authorities in the field of school health work have for some time advocated that the family and the private physician assume more responsibility for the health appraisal of school children. A monograph approved for the Wisconsin Cooperative School Health Program presents a point of view on school health examinations, as follows:

> Under an ideal of attainment there would be no need for a school health examination program, as each parent would assume his responsibility for continuous and frequent examinations of his children from birth to maturity. However, in the realization that this ideal may never be fully attained, there is need for schools to equip themselves to assume a share of the responsibility not shouldered by parents, in order to develop plans through which all children will be given the benefits of health examinations. But, instead of assuming that all or a large share of parents will not provide for the health of their children, the school should recognize its responsibility in encouraging a community-wide health examination program utilizing the services of family physicians. Experience in some Wisconsin communities has shown that many parents will respond to suggestions of this kind.
>
> Even though health examinations given under school auspices might be thorough and fact-finding, it is preferable to encourage the relationship of the individual child to his family physician. Such a relationship will provide a more personal contact than can be enjoyed through school examinations. It is also a relationship which can be started before entrance to school and continued after school days are over. Often the family physician's intimate knowledge of family situations explains, in part, physical manifestations revealed by examination.[4]

The health appraisal of the child is the starting point for continuing health guidance and becomes the basis for pro-

[4] *School Health Examinations* (2d ed.; Madison, Wis.: State Medical Society of Wisconsin, 1951; revised April, 1951, and reprinted August, 1954), p. 5.

fessional suggestions regarding habits of living, and for recommendations about preventive treatment and remedial medical care when necessary.

Standards for Examination

At present there is no uniformity of opinion about the number of times during his school career that a child should be medically examined for the purpose of appraisal. In some states, New York and Oregon for example, the law of the state requires that each child be examined annually; in others, Pennsylvania for example, the requirement is for an examination every second year; in Connecticut examinations are required at least once in three years; Wisconsin suggests examinations at intervals of three or four years.

Where the state requirement calls for a routine health appraisal at intervals greater than one year, attention is usually directed to the need for continuous observation of pupils by nurse and teacher. In this arrangement, medical services should be made available at any time for pupils who, in the opinion of nurse or teacher, have need for a special examination. The National Committee on School Health Policies makes a recommendation, as follows:

During their school years students should have a minimum of four medical examinations; one at the time of entrance to school, one in the intermediate grades, one at the beginning of adolescence and one before leaving school. Pupils who have serious defects or abnormalities, who have suffered from serious or repeated illnesses, or who engage in vigorous athletic programs require more frequent examinations. The physician is the best judge of the need for repeated examinations and of the frequency with which they should be given. Additional examinations, even annual examinations, may be arranged if money, time, and personnel permit, but the quality of medical procedures and judgment should not be sacrificed to a desire for frequent and complete coverage of the entire school.[5]

[5] *Suggested School Health Policies, A Charter for School Health* (2d ed.; Chicago: American Medical Association, and New York: Health Education Council, 1950), pp. 28-29.

The American Medical Association recommends health examinations at intervals of three years during the school career of the child.

At present the tendency seems to be in the direction of requiring fewer regularly scheduled medical examinations than were formerly considered necessary and in the direction of placing more emphasis on their comprehensiveness and quality. The trend today is very definitely toward scheduling examinations on the child's entrance to school and at two- or three-year intervals during his school career. This arrangement requires screening as a supplement to the regularly scheduled examinations. *Screening* is a procedure used by teacher or nurse to obtain information about a child's health. For example, particularly at the opening of school in the fall and also at other times during the school year, a teacher inspects the hands and the face of every child in her classroom to find out whether there are signs of skin infection. Any child who shows signs of an unusual skin condition is screened out and is referred for medical opinion. Tests used in a screening procedure, such as vision and hearing tests (see Chap. 4), are intended only to screen out children for referral to medical opinion. Such tests, as they are used by the teacher, are not intended to be diagnostic.

The question of how much time should be given to the examination by the physician has received the attention of various professional groups. Any plan which does not allow adequate time for the physician to complete an examination is unsatisfactory. The School Health Practices Act of Pennsylvania requires that no more than an average of four pupils be examined per hour. The State Medical Society of Wisconsin recommends at least 15 minutes per child. The reason for placing emphasis on the amount of time given to the examination by the physician is that in the past the number of periodic examinations required in many schools was disproportionate to the physician services available to the school. The result was a hurried and superficial examination in many cases. It is generally realized that the amount of time given to a health examination is not necessarily the sole criterion of the worth of the examination, but that adequate time for unhurried work is an important factor in the health examination program.

The trend seems to be toward allotting enough time for the examination so that the following criteria are met: (1) provision for an educational experience for the child, (2) time to discuss items of the examining procedure with the parent, (3) an unhurried and personalized experience for the pupil, and (4) a comprehensive examination which is appropriate to conditions under which the examining is done and which meets high technical standards. Specifically, a minimum of 15 minutes for each child seems to be necessary if these standards are to be met.

The scope of the examination is indicated by the items for which the physician is responsible on the Health Appraisal Summarizing Chart (see Table 2).

In some states the health record card has been developed cooperatively by the state board of education and the state board of health, and the cards are made available in quantity to local school boards. In some instances the local board of education adopts a health record card prepared by members of its own staff or by the local board of health. The health record is cumulative. Space is provided on the cards for recording, during the pupil's school career, all examination findings, pertinent items of health history, and any other items of value in health guidance.

———————————————————————————————→

The items listed on the following chart in Column 1 are recommended as essential to an appraisal of the school child's health status. Column 2 includes those items which any teacher may be trained to check and record; Column 3 includes those items which a trained physical education teacher may be expected to check reliably; Column 4 contains those items which the nurse may be expected to inspect; Column 5 lists those items for which only the physician may be responsible.

TABLE 2
HEALTH APPRAISAL SUMMARIZING CHART

Essential Items for Health Appraisal (1)	Inspection Items			Examination Items
	For which Any Teacher May Be Responsible (2)	For which Physical Education Teacher May Be Responsible (3)	For which Nurse May Be Responsible (4)	For which Only Physician May Be Responsible (5)
Height	x	x	x	
Weight	x	x	x	
Nutrition				x
Vision	x	x	x	
Hearing	x	x	x	
Skin	x	x	x	
Heart (Medical)				x
Pulse rate (Resting)		x	x	
Pulse rate (After exercise)		x	x	
Lungs				x
Posture	x	x	x	
Muscle tone		x	x	
Orthopedic defects				x
Hernia				x
Eyes and lids	x	x	x	
Ears (External exam.) ..	x	x	x	
Ears (Internal exam.) ..				x
Teeth (Obvious decay) .	x	x	x	
Gum inflammation	x	x	x	
Tonsils				x
Nose				x
Thyroid				x
Lymph nodes				x
Glands of internal secretion				x
Nervous system (Organic)				x
Nervous system (Behavior)	x	x	x	
Speech	x	x	x	

NOTE: Marked orthopedic defects, enlarged lymph nodes, obesity, enlarged thyroid, protruding hernia and certain growth abnormalities which are obviously apparent to the teacher, physical educator, or nurse should be promptly referred to the family and the physician for further investigation.

SOURCE: National Education Association and American Medical Association, Joint Committee on Health Problems in Education, *Health Appraisal of School Children* (Washington, D. C.: National Education Association, and Chicago: American Medical Association, 1950), pp. 28-29.

If pupil personnel work has been developed to a high degree of effectiveness—as is the case in some school systems —the health record card becomes one of the sources of general information about the student. The health record thus supplements the academic and social records for use in pupil guidance.

The medical examination aspect of health appraisal is conducted mainly for educational purposes. The child gains a nontechnical understanding of the reason for various procedures which are followed in the examination. Under desirable conditions of examining, which are characterized by an unhurried, friendly atmosphere and in which respect for the individual child is dominant, he is encouraged to regard the experience as a pleasant one. If this is his reaction, the concept of prevention in personal health matters, which requires periodic medical guidance throughout life, should not be difficult to establish. There is further educational value in the health examination whenever guidance is given to parents about the health practices of their children or about the correction of remediable defects if this is necessary. In order to achieve these educational purposes, careful planning is necessary. By means of preliminary classroom activity (a demonstration examination and discussion, for example) the classroom teacher and school physician can make the total experience for each child one which has more meaning for him and one in which he does not play an entirely passive part. Needless to say, such a procedure must be carefully arranged in order to center pupil attention on the purpose of the demonstration and to avoid possible criticism from parents, which might result from using a pupil in the demonstration.

Teacher Observation and Inspection

One of the more important parts of a health appraisal program is teacher observation. The elementary classroom teacher is in a unique position in reference to the school's responsibility for child health problems. She is in contact with the child for a longer period of time than is any other person in the school, is aware of his home conditions, is in a position to know what for him is normal appearance and behavior, and consequently, is better able to detect deviation from normal. Most important of all, she knows him as a person and has a highly developed sense of professional responsibility for his welfare.

School administrators and health authorities are in agreement that the classroom teacher is in a most advantageous position to supplement the work of the school health specialist. As a result of her contacts with the child and her knowledge about him, the teacher can supplement, in many ways, information obtained by the physician at the time of the health examination. Factors in the life of the child that are of value in his total appraisal—such factors as the amount of absence from school and stated reasons for it, periodic complaints, relationships with other pupils, and the existence of conditions at home or in school that may be responsible for a disturbed emotional state—should be made available by the teacher to the physician or the nurse. This supplementary information can be valuable to the physician.

In addition to supplying information about the pupil which the physician needs and cannot always obtain in his examination of the child, the teacher can make a substantial contribution to the health appraisal program by use of specific screening procedures in her classroom and by referral to the physician of those pupils who have need of medical opinion. The effectiveness of teacher observation is related to the knowledge and the understanding that the teacher has acquired through professional training and experience with child behavior and appearance. Interpretation of unusualness in appearance or behavior is not called for in teacher observation. The reasons for unusualness are supplied by the diagnostician. The teacher's responsibility is to refer, to the source responsible for supplying or obtaining diagnosis and care, any child who gives evidence of appearing or behaving at variance with what is normal for him. In doing this she is performing one of the more important parts of the total health guidance program.

Experimental work shows comparatively little evidence as to the effectiveness of the teacher in physical inspection of children, although school administrators and health specialists agree that she is a key person in the over-all elementary school health program. Miller, reporting the results of a University School experiment, states:

> The teacher made valid judgments on thirty-six validated items of the physical inspection. She did a commendable job in terms of efficiency (segregating deviations), accuracy (recognizing normal conditions), and effectiveness (making total judgments), regardless of the items inspected or the degree of discrimination requested.[6]

Although experimental evidence indicating the importance of the role played by the classroom teacher in the physical inspection of pupils is rather limited, the school principal and the administrator of the school health program are keenly aware of her capabilities and rely heavily on her judgment. Through members of its professional staff, particularly the school nurse, the health service department of the school is ready to be of assistance to the teacher in the more technical aspects of her health work with children. This department is aware of the contribution she can make to effective health service. Regularly scheduled meetings between classroom teacher and nurse insure an interchange of information about pupils. For the teacher this provides useful technical information about child health. For ex-

---

[6] Ben W. Miller, "A Critical Evaluation of the Effectiveness of the Teacher in the Physical Inspection of Public School Children," *Research Quarterly of the American Association for Health, Physical Education, and Recreation,* XIV (1943), 136.

ample, the classroom teacher will have a better basis for health guidance activities when reports about the medical examination and about the home conditions of pupils are made available to her by the nurse. On the other hand, information given to the nurse by the teacher about the behavior of the child in his group relationships may be of value in the over-all appraisal of the child by the health specialists.

There are, in general, two methods, the formal and the informal, used by the classroom teacher in her observation of pupils. The observational techniques are the same in both methods, but the procedures are slightly different.

The *formal observation,* sometimes referred to as *teacher inspection,* is part of the daily classroom program and is chiefly concerned with detecting early signs of childhood communicable disease. This procedure, which usually follows the opening of school in the morning, is a recognized part of the classroom program and has a specified time allotment. There is the possibility that this formal activity may become a perfunctory activity, that it may be considered one of the "annoying musts," and that the teacher may consider her job done upon completion of the inspection. This possibility has resulted recently in less emphasis being placed on this type of pupil observation.

The second method is that of continuous, *informal observation,* one in which the teacher is alert to changes in the appearance and behavior of pupils. She may at some specific time during the day, preferably in the morning, observe each child informally to determine whether there is a need for referring him to nurse or physician for further observation. At other times during the day, deviations from normal appearance and behavior are likewise noted by the teacher and appropriate action taken. In the technique of continuous observation there is the advantage of a more complete understanding of the child and of a development of a sense of responsibility for his welfare. The procedure of continuous observation is particularly appropriate in the control of child-hood communicable disease in view of the unpredictability of the onset of these diseases.

A table issued by the Metropolitan Life Insurance Company lists conditions which the teacher should notice and which are the basis for her referral of the child (see Table 3). The procedure of informal observation is used not only to detect signs of physical unusualness, but also to detect evidence of social or emotional maladjustment (see Chap. 10).

Follow-up Program

The health appraisal of the child is the starting point for preventive or corrective work, but until such work is actually carried out, appraisal has limited value. Unless vigorous follow-up work for the correction of remediable defects is recognized as an important part of the health service program, health appraisal will fail to achieve its purposes. In the vast majority of instances the correction of remediable defects in children is initiated by parents. The most favorable circumstance for follow-up work exists when the parent is present at the child's examination. When the parent is present, specific recommendations can be made to him by the physician, and questions can be directed to the physician by the parent. However, in many instances a parent is not present at the child's examination. This means that the recommendations of the physician must be conveyed to the parent by the nurse or the teacher.

Although the teacher in her contacts with parents can be effective in the follow-up program, the bulk of this work is the responsibility of the nurse. In actual practice the nurse will spend much of her time making visits to homes of parents who were not present at the examinations of their children and who attempt to make little if any contact with the school. She is faced with a multitude of different problems in her home visits and must combine the maximum of technical skill and patience in her work as a health educator. Although meeting indifference, ignorance, prejudice, and at times marked distrust, she must rely solely on persuasion and the "inevitability of gradualness" for much of her accomplishment.

In connection with follow-up work, the question as to the use of health record cards by different members of the school staff sometimes arises. At times a marked reluctance is evidenced by the health specialists to agree to any plan whereby the health records of children are made easily available to the classroom teacher. This reluctance is an extension to school health work of the policy of maintaining a confidential relationship between physician and patient. In addition, there is fear that the teacher, a lay person, may misinterpret notations on the health record card. Both problems, if they actually exist, suggest the need for in-service training for the teacher and for establishing a better working relationship among all persons concerned with child health. An effective method of meeting the objection raised in connection with the use of health records by the teacher is to have all information on the cards made entirely clear to teachers through nurse-teacher conferences, at which time it can be indicated to teachers that all health records contain professional data and are to be discretely used.

In some cases the record cards are filed in the nurse's office; in others, in the office of the principal; and, in some instances, the records are kept by the teacher in the classroom. If effective health guidance is to be achieved, the record of the child must be easily available to all school staff members. It would seem clear that any limitation on the availability of pupil record cards to teachers would not be in the best interests of the school child.

TABLE 3

WHAT TEACHERS SEE

POINT OF OBSERVATION	PHYSICAL SIGNS	BEHAVIOR	COMPLAINTS
General appearance and behavior	Excessive thinness; excessive overweight; very small or very large in body build for age; pallor; weary expression; poor posture; dark circles or puffiness under eyes	Acts tired or apathetic; is easily irritated; makes frequent trips to toilet; has persistent nervous habits, such as muscular twitching or biting of nails or lips; is subject to spasms (fits), fainting spells, or frequent nosebleeds; gets short of breath after mild exertion and climbing stairs; lacks appetite; vomits frequently; has frequent accidents	Feels tired; doesn't want to play; has aches or pains; feels sick to stomach; feels dizzy
Hair and scalp	Stringy, lusterless hair; small bald spots; crusty sores on scalp; nits in hair	Scratches head frequently	Head itches
Ears	Discharge from ears; cotton in ear; tired, strained expression long before day is over; watchful, sometimes bewildered expression	Is persistently inattentive; asks to have question repeated; habitually fails to respond when questioned; mispronounces common words; cocks one ear toward speaker	Has earache; has buzzing or ringing in ears; ears feel stuffy; hears noises in head
Eyes	Inflamed or watery eyes; frequent styes; crusted lids; cross-eye	Holds book too close to eyes; squints at book or blackboard; persistently rubs or blinks eyes; reads poorly	Head aches; eyes ache or smart; cannot see well (blurred vision)

Mouth and teeth	Cavities in teeth; excessive tartar at necks of teeth; malocclusion (uneven bite); irregular teeth; bleeding or inflamed gums; swollen jaw; sores in mouth; cracking of lips and corners of mouth	Acts depressed or resentful if many missing teeth or severe malocclusion subjects him to teasing or adverse comments from other children. This behavior is especially likely to occur in adolescence	Has toothache; mouth or gums feel sore
Nose and throat (upper respiratory tract)	Frequent or long-continued colds; persistent nasal discharge	Is frequently absent from school because of a cold; constantly clears throat or has frequent coughing or sneezing spells; is always sniffling or blowing nose; breathes persistently through mouth	Throat feels sore or scratchy; has difficulty in swallowing; nose feels stuffy or sore
Skin	Rashes or inflamed skin areas; scales and crusts; persistent sores, pimples and blackheads on face; boils; hives; persistent warts; accidental injuries such as cuts, scratches, bruises, burns	Is always scratching himself; is subject to skin irritations (hives, eczema, puzzling rashes, etc.) which suggest sensitivity to one or more substances (allergic manifestations); is easily bruised	Skin itches or burns; is concerned about pimples, blackheads, and other skin conditions which affect personal appearance

SOURCE: George M. Wheatley *et al.*, *What Teachers See* (New York: Metropolitan Life Insurance Company, 1954), p. 31. Courtesy of the Metropolitan Life Insurance Company.

Cooperative Activity

One of the more effective ways of obtaining group effort for the school health program is through a health council or a health committee. In general, the membership of such a council includes members of the school staff and representatives from interested community groups (see Chap. 11).

Although the organization and the specific functions of a health council should be determined by its members, who are familiar with the particular needs of their school community, the statement which follows may be useful as a general guide:

1. The council should include representation from parents, the schools, the health department, professional associations (medical and dental societies), and community health and welfare agencies.

2. Each group named above should select its own representatives. Council officers should be elected by the group for specified periods of time.

3. The council should meet at regular times and with prepared agenda.

4. Each group should be permitted to present for council consideration any problem dealing with the health of school children. Particular attention should be given to problems requiring joint action by the schools and other community agencies and those that involve participation by two or more professional groups.

5. The purposes, objectives, and policies of the council should be stated clearly and reviewed periodically.

6. Use should be made of committees, but these should always report to the council as a whole.

7. Although long-term projects are necessary and appropriate, projects which can be completed successfully in a short period of time should also receive attention. Publicity should be given throughout the community to the council's accomplishments.

8. Emphasis should be placed on solving particular problems rather than on organization or on routine procedures.[7]

A health council makes the health resources of a community available to school health specialists and to the classroom teacher. Health problems of school children are seen in relation to other community health problems, and in council planning for community health, the school child and his problems become one of the common interests of health council members. The school health guidance program will be more effective when such resources are utilized.

SELECTED REFERENCES

AMERICAN MEDICAL ASSOCIATION. *Third National Conference on Physicians and Schools.* Conference Report. Chicago: The Association, 1951.

COMMISSION ON HEALTH IN SCHOOLS. *Health in Schools,* rev. ed. Twentieth Yearbook of the American Association of School Administrators. Washington, D. C.: National Education Association, 1951.

CROMWELL, GERTRUDE E. *The Health of the School Child.* Philadelphia: W. B. Saunders Co., 1946.

DEWEESE, A. O. "Teacher's Health Inspection," *Journal of School Health,* XXIII (October, 1953), 245-49.

NATIONAL COMMITTEE ON SCHOOL HEALTH POLICIES. *Suggested School Health Policies, A Charter for School Health,* 2d ed. Chicago: American Medical Association, and New York: Health Education Council, 1950.

School Health Examinations. Madison, Wis.: State Medical Society of Wisconsin, 1951.

WHEATLEY, GEORGE M., and HALLOCK, GRACE T. *Health Observation of School Children.* New York: McGraw-Hill Book Co., Inc., 1951.

WILSON, CHARLES C. (ed.). American Medical Association and National Education Association, Joint Committee on Health Problems in Education. *Health Education,* 4th ed. Washington, D. C.: National Education Association, 1948.

WILSON, CHARLES C. (ed.). *School Health Services.* Report of the Joint Committee on Health Problems in Education of the National Education Association and the American Medical Association. Washington, D. C.: National Education Association, and Chicago: American Medical Association, 1953.

[7] Charles C. Wilson, "The Council Can Be Proud." Reprinted from *Ideas for Teachers,* "The Nassau County School Health Council," Vol. XIX, No. 2, published by the Nassau County Tuberculosis and Public Health Association, Roslyn, New York.

Chapter 4

THE CONSERVATION OF VISION AND HEARING

Modern schooling is largely a series of experiences that requires extensive use of the eyes and the ears. A deficiency of vision or hearing obviously limits the child's participation in the school program and results in less than complete educational opportunity. The child's attempt to compensate for a physical deficiency requires extra effort and puts his climate of learning under a strain.

Conservation of Vision

Ideally, each child should be examined by an ophthalmologist during his preschool years or before entering school. He should have routine vision tests by the school nurse or the teacher each year throughout his elementary school years. Each child who registers in another school system for the first time should have a vision test. In addition to the children who show less than normal visual acuity when tested by nurse or teacher, there may be others who, because they complain or show signs of visual difficulty, need to be referred for medical opinion. By these procedures, serious or potentially serious visual difficulty can be recognized, and the child can then be referred for early diagnosis and treatment.

Vision Defects

The most common vision defects among school children are *farsightedness* (hyperopia), *nearsightedness* (myopia), *squint* (strabismus), and *astigmatism* (a condition in which there is irregular curvature of cornea or lens). The normal eye receives light rays from the object being viewed. These rays come to focus on the retina, after passing through the front of the eye, as indicated in Figure 6.

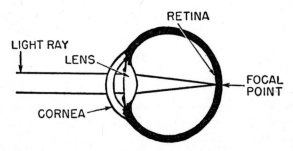

FIGURE 6. Diagram of Normal Eye

In cases of farsightedness, the eyeball is shorter from front to back than is required for its optical system. The result is that the focal point does not fall on the retina but in back of it. This causes imperfect vision (see Fig. 7). Although farsightedness is the most common vision defect of children, its degree of optical deficiency decreases as the child grows

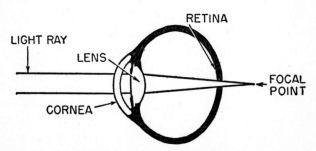

FIGURE 7. Diagram of Hyperopic Eye

older.[1] A child attempting to obtain a clear image calls on greater than normal accommodation and, by so doing, may experience undue fatigue in the muscles involved. If a child has a low tolerance for fatigue and engages in visual activity requiring close work, farsightedness can produce marked discomfort and result in poor adjustment to the classroom situation.

A nearsighted child has an eyeball that is relatively long from front to back. In this condition the focal point falls in front of the retina (see Fig. 8). There is no method by

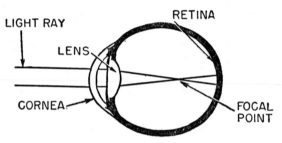

FIGURE 8. Diagram of Myopic Eye

which the eye itself can compensate for this condition, but the child brings the object being viewed closer to the eye and, by so doing, produces a clearer image on the retina. The nearsighted child does not experience strain as does the farsighted child who, when he views objects closely, must call extensively on his powers of accommodation to compensate for hyperopia. The myopic child may disregard objects on which he cannot focus. This tendency can have an adverse influence on his attitude toward many things which are part of his school experience. Material on the blackboard holds neither meaning nor interest for him because he cannot see it clearly, and he may be particularly

[1] In childhood the optical system reaches its adult size much earlier than does the eyeball. With most children the eyeball continues to grow until the correct size is reached and farsightedness is no longer a problem.

uninterested in games because of his inability to focus beyond a limited distance.

Astigmatism occurs when there is irregularity in the curved surfaces of the cornea or the lens of the eye. The result is improper focusing of light rays on the retina due to differences in refraction caused by the irregular curved surfaces through which light rays enter the eye. A child with a significant amount of astigmatism attempts to overcome the resulting blurred image through involuntary adjustment by the eye itself and through such voluntary actions as narrowing of the lids and moving of the head. Such procedures do not effectively increase the clarity of the object being viewed. The effect of uncorrected astigmatism is eye fatigue, indicated by such signs as nervousness, headaches, and sensitiveness to light.

The action of the external muscles of the eye, which determine the point on which the individual is focusing, is a synchronized action in normal vision. That is, both eyes look in the same direction at the same time (binocular vision). In cases where the action of the external eye muscles is not synchronized, the result is termed *squint,* or *strabismus.* The eye in this condition may tend to deviate to either side, or up or down, and such deviation may easily be observed by the teacher. The common type is that in which the eye turns inward toward the nose. This condition usually develops during preschool years. In some cases, strabismus is *latent,* and for this reason, cannot be readily observed by the lay person. Poor health may tend to make the strabismus noticeable, although the condition is apparently absent at other times. With either observable or latent strabismus only one eye may be in use, or the eyes may function alternately. If both eyes are used in turn, vision may not be impaired in either eye. If only one eye is used, the effectiveness of the unused eye becomes less, and binocular vision may be lost if this condition persists too long.

Medical care under the direction of an eye specialist is necessary immediately upon discovery that strabismus exists. Of particular importance in the prevention of strabismus are testing techniques that indicate unequal visual acuity in the two eyes, poor coordination, poor fusion, and significant error in refraction. This type of comprehensive examination cannot be given by the classroom teacher. Careful ophthalmologic procedures are called for and should be part of the health examination during the preschool years or at the time of the child's entrance to school.

Vision Tests

The most common test for vision, one that has been used in schools for many years, is the Snellen test. It is designed to test visual acuity at 20 feet and does this effectively.[2] The equipment and instructions necessary for administering the Snellen test are given in Monograph No. 485, *A Guide for Eye Inspection and Vision Testing*, issued by the National Society for the Prevention of Blindness.

"Examiners have pointed out that an individual can pass the Snellen test even though he has significant amounts of hyperopia. To meet this objection, a frame fitted with "plus" sphere lenses is placed before the eyes of each pupil who has 20/20 vision. The child with normal vision is not able to read the 20/20 line or better on the chart. This constitutes "passing" the test. Those who can read the 20/20 line or better on the chart "fail" the test and should be referred for a complete eye examination.[3]" Standards for referral are recommended by the Committee on School Vision Tests of the New England Ophthalmological Society and the Massachusetts Medical Society. A child in grades up to the

[2] Thomas E. Shaffer, "Study of Vision Testing Procedures," *American Journal of Public Health*, XXXVIII (1948), 1141-46.

[3] John D. Schonwald, "Visual Examination for School Children," *Journal of School Health*, XVIII (1948), 99-102.

third should be referred for further examination if he has visual acuity less than 20/40 in either eye or can read the 20/20 line or better on the chart with a plus 2.25 sphere over either eye. A child in the fourth grade or beyond should be referred if he has visual acuity less than 20/30 in either eye or can read the 20/20 line or better with a plus 1.75 sphere over either eye.

Two other types of tests have been developed and are being used for vision-testing in schools. The Massachusetts vision test was "designed to meet the need for improved procedures which will bridge the gap between present inadequate provisions and the time somewhere in the future when the eyes of all children will be examined by a qualified eye specialist."[4]

The other testing device in school use utilizes test charts which are viewed through binocular lenses. This test and the Massachusetts vision test are designed to make possible a more comprehensive examination than is obtainable with the Snellen test.

Referral to Specialists

In the program of follow-up with children whose vision test indicates less than normal visual acuity, the nurse and the teacher should remember that the result of their testing program does not constitute a diagnosis of a child's visual difficulties. The parents of a child whose test indicates that he has less than normal visual acuity should be referred to an eye specialist. The teacher or the school nurse may be called upon to discuss with parents the various kinds of specialists who contribute to eye care.

The National Society for the Prevention of Blindness defines the kinds of eye specialists and provides a brief description of their fields of activity, as follows:

[4] Laura Oak, "The Massachusetts Vision Test," *American Journal of Public Health*, XXXII (1942), 1109.

1. The *ophthalmologist* or *oculist* is a physician, licensed to practice medicine and surgery, who specializes in treatment of eye diseases and optical defects. He may use the initials M.D. after his name.
2. The *optometrist* is licensed to examine the eyes and prescribe and provide lenses or visual training needed. Since he is not a medical doctor, if he suspects eye disease he will refer the patient to a physician for medical care. He may use the initials O.D. after his name.
3. The *optician* is trained to grind, fit, and supply eyeglasses.[5]

Classroom Lighting

Many studies have indicated that adequate lighting of classrooms will materially reduce eye fatigue in children, with its accompanying undesirable consequences. The classroom teacher is usually not able to control such factors as the relationship between floor space and glass area, or the reflection of light from the walls and furniture in the room. When there is need for it, she should be sure to use artificial lighting provided in the classroom and should prevent undesirable reflection of light from outside the building into the classroom. Window shades mounted in the center of the window is a desirable arrangement. This allows either the lower or the upper half of the window to be shaded. The following suggestions concerning the role of the classroom teacher in the program of classroom lighting are made by the National Society for the Prevention of Blindness:

Every teacher can improve seeing conditions in her classroom by:

1. Keeping upper portions of windows unshaded except when the sun is shining directly on them.
2. Drawing shades over the lower portions of the glass area only when necessary to diffuse direct sunlight or to reduce glare from snow, sky, or adjacent buildings.
3. Checking illumination levels in all parts of the room periodically with a light meter.

[5] *Take Care of Your Eyes*, Publication No. 2 (New York: National Society for the Prevention of Blindness, Inc., 1952), first page.

4. Making special seating arrangements for left-handed pupils so that light will fall over the right shoulder.
5. Keeping window sills free of all obstructions to light.
6. Arranging seats and desks so that no pupil will face a window or work in his own shadow.
7. Cleaning chalkboards frequently.
8. Eliminating books, charts, maps, etc., that are so soiled as to provide poor brightness contrast.
9. Providing copyholders and easels to maintain good posture and optimum lighting for close eye tasks.
10. Making all board writing large and clear and placing it in the line of vision of the pupils.
11. Planning the daily program so as to alternate periods of close eye work with activities less demanding visually.
12. Switching on artificial lights whenever brightness levels fall below standard in any part of the room.
13. Standing and sitting in positions which direct pupils' vision away from the windows.
14. Planning for periodic adjustments of seats and desks to provide for best use of available light.
15. Placing pupils with eye difficulties in the best-lighted places from the standpoint of their specific defects.
16. Allowing pupils to change their seats whenever they desire more light or less light.
17. Selecting work places to make best use of available light.
18. Covering chalkboards not being used, to conserve available light.
19. Covering glass doors on cabinets and removing pictures covered with glass.
20. Selecting and using only those textbooks, maps, charts, posters, etc., that have nongloss surfaces, appropriate type size, and desirable contrast.
21. Noting when lamps or tubes become blackened or defective and calling for correction from the custodian.
22. Developing in the children a sense of responsibility for assisting in the maintenance of good seeing conditions.[6]

Conservation of Hearing

Hearing loss of varying degrees is found in millions of persons in the United States. There were in the United

[6] *Classroom Lighting*, Publication No. 498 (New York: National Society for the Prevention of Blindness, Inc., 1950), pp. 14-15.

States in 1951 approximately ten million people hard of hearing to some extent in one or both ears.[7] In many of these persons the loss can be traced to lack of medical care in childhood. For this reason the elementary school has a unique opportunity and a distinct responsibility in the area of hearing conservation. If such a program is effectively carried out, much of the hearing loss and many of the emotional and social problems of childhood and adult life which have their origin in defective hearing will be markedly reduced.

A fairly reliable, though possibly conservative, estimate of the school population having some degree of hearing loss is 5 per cent.[8] This fact is of immediate importance and indicates that there are many children in elementary school with inadequate hearing. It follows naturally that many of these children are not profiting to the extent that they should from their school experiences.

The discovery of cases of hearing loss is the first step in a school program for the conservation of hearing. This procedure involves the classroom teacher, whether she actually does the testing herself or cooperates with the person who does.

Types of Hearing Defects

The more common type of hearing defect is the type referred to as *conduction deafness.* As the term implies, the defect exists somewhere in the sound-wave-conducting part of the hearing mechanism, the outer and the middle ear. Middle ear infection (*otitis media*) is the most common cause of this type of hearing impairment. This infection manifests itself as a severe earache, although there are other

[7] Edmund P. Fowler, "Conservation of Hearing in the Schools. What Has Been Done, and What Now Should and Should Not Be Done," *Journal of School Health,* XXIV (1954), 95.

[8] S. R. Silverman, "Hard-of-Hearing Children," in *Hearing and Deafness,* ed. Hallowell Davis (New York: Murray Hill Books, Inc., 1947), pp. 354-55.

causes of earache. A child with a "running" ear or earache should be referred for medical advice. Unless such action is taken there is the possibility of permanent damage to the tissues of the middle ear and of irremediable hearing loss.

Less common is *nerve deafness,* in which there is injury to nerve tissue transmitting impulses to the brain or injury to the brain tissue involved in hearing perception.[9] Injury to nerve tissue can result from acute infection, such as scarlet fever, poliomyelitis, and meningitis.

Conduction deafness, which causes a loss in hearing low tones, results in difficulty in distinguishing and reproducing vowels. Nerve deafness, which causes a loss in hearing high tones, results in difficulty in distinguishing and reproducing consonants. A child who has difficulty in hearing certain parts of words used in conversation has difficulty in reproducing the sounds of these parts. His conversation is a reproduction of words as he hears them through his faulty hearing mechanism.

The typical signs of hearing loss in a child, such as failure to carry out instructions, inattention, and faulty articulation, are reasonably well understood, and if the signs persist, constitute a sound basis of referral for a special hearing test. In addition, routine testing is desirable annually for each child during the elementary school years, although many school systems prefer to follow a plan of testing biennially.

Hearing Tests

Testing for hearing acuity may be done by using the *watch test* or the *whisper test.* The result of either test should be recognized as a rough measure of hearing acuity. Either test is relatively simple to conduct, and where the use of an audiometer is not possible, the watch test or the

[9] Charles R. Hayman, Benjamin S. Rich, and Eleanor Stark, "A Conservation of Hearing Program for School Children," *American Journal of Public Health,* XLI (1951), 1519.

whisper test, used as a screening device, serves to identify a pupil whose hearing acuity is less than that of the majority of his group.

The use of an audiometer results in a more objective test of hearing. The *phonograph audiometer,* designed for group testing, requires special arrangements for recording results when this audiometer is used in testing children in grades below the third. The *pure-tone,* or *discrete-frequency, audiometer* may be used to give group tests or individual tests. The preferred method of testing calls for the use of the pure-tone audiometer.

The watch test is carried out in the following manner. A watch with a reasonably loud tick is used. The child is placed with his back toward the examiner, his eyes closed, and one hand cupped over the ear not being tested. The watch is held at a distance at which the child can hear the tick easily. The examiner then moves the watch away from the child until he can no longer hear the tick. The examiner next moves the watch toward the child and notes the point at which he *first* hears the tick. The distance between this point and the child is recorded.

The distance at which a child should hear the tick in order to pass the watch test is the distance at which the tick is *first* heard by the majority of the group of children being tested. Depending on the loudness of the tick and on the relative quietness of the room where the testing is done, the distance may vary from 1 to 3 feet.

This test is in no way a qualitative test of hearing. It is intended to screen children presumed to have some degree of hearing loss, and becomes the basis for the referral for medical opinion.

The whisper test depends for its reliability on the ability of the examiner to produce the same volume of sound each time she whispers a word or a number. Reasonable consistency in the degree of loudness of the whisper can be obtained by producing the sound after the end of a normal expiration. That is, the whisper is produced by using reserve expiratory air forcibly exhaled.

Arrangements for the test involve determining a point at which the pupil will stand. A 20-foot distance from this point is then measured off on the floor. At intervals of 2 feet, marks are made—the first mark 2 feet away from the point at which the pupil stands; the second, 4 feet away, and so on, and the last 20 feet away.

The child stands sidewise to the teacher and cups his hand over the ear not being tested. The teacher begins the test at a distance where the child hears the whisper easily. She instructs him to report what he hears. She repeats the whisper as she moves away from the child and records for each ear the greatest distance, up to 20 feet, at which he can repeat the whispered word or number.

The teacher determines whether she wishes to use numbers or one-syllable words. It is important that the child recognize the word or the number that is used. Both consonants and vowels should be utilized in order that the test detect signs of conduction deafness and signs of nerve deafness.

Recording the results of the whisper test requires that a standard for passing be established. This is done by determining the distance from the 20-foot mark at which 80 per cent of the group were able to hear the whisper. This point must be determined each time the test is given to a group, because of the possibility of variation in the whisper or in other conditions under which the test is given.

A child who must stand nearer to the examiner than did 80 per cent of his group fails to pass. Although he fails to pass the test, he does not necessarily have a hearing defect. He should be referred for a more accurate determination of hearing efficiency.

Audiometer testing may be carried on as a group test or as a test for a single individual. In some schools this type of testing is done by the classroom teacher. However, the relative infrequency of audiometer testing, which is usually done routinely no more often than once a year, plus the need for a high degree of skill, much of which comes with practice, suggest the services of a specialist. A member of the school nursing staff or a trained specialist from an official or voluntary health agency may be assigned to this work. An agency specialist would work under the general direction of the school administrator and in accordance with the educational policies of the board of education.

Hearing loss is measured in decibels.[10] When the phonograph audiometer is used, a loss of 9 decibels in the poorer ear is considered a positive finding, and the child should be referred for further testing. In the phonograph audiometer test, voice sounds are transmitted from a record through the phonograph and to the earphones of the approximately forty children, who transcribe what they hear on mimeographed direction sheets. Because the child being examined must record numbers on the test sheet, the group test is not considered reliable below the third grade unless an older child transcribes what the younger child states he hears.[11]

Some children fail the group test because of a cold, because of unfamiliarity with the procedure, or because of noisy surroundings. These children are retested under improved conditions.

In all types of surveys about 10 to 15 per cent of children screened for the first time are likely to fail to pass the test for a variety of reasons—immaturity, excitement, emotional instability, inability to concentrate, inability to understand directions, lack of rapport, lack of experience with the specific sound stimulus, and a real hearing loss.

[10] A decibel is the least change in loudness or sound for any given tone that can be detected by the normal human ear.
[11] Gertrude E. Cromwell, *The Health of the School Child* (Philadelphia: W. B. Saunders Co., 1946), pp. 120-21.

About 3 to 5 per cent of children may show a real hearing loss when the survey has been completed, but only approximately 1.5 per cent of the school population will need adjusted educational programs.[12]

Children who fail the group test a second time are referred for an individual test with the pure-tone audiometer. The pure-tone audiometer produces a steady and somewhat musical sound by the use of a vacuum tube. The examiner may interrupt the sound when he wishes to do so, by moving a switch. The frequency and the intensity of the sound may also be changed at the will of the examiner. This feature, when coupled with the construction of an audiogram for the individual being tested, gives a diagnostic function to testing with the pure-tone audiometer. The range of this instrument in both frequency (pitch) and intensity (loudness) makes possible the testing for sounds above and below the normal range of conversation. The pure-tone audiometer, which is considered by many as the best testing device for school use, may be used in all grades. The following is a good description of the testing technique.

Usually the right ear is tested first. In ordinary school situations where soundproofing and other controls are not present, the intensity dial is set at a 15-decibel loss position. The tone dial of the audiometer is changed rather quickly from 256 vibrations per second to 4,096 inclusive. This procedure is sometimes referred to as the sweep-check method. In the interest of rapid screening the extremes of low and high frequencies are frequently omitted. The child's face is observed constantly and he is asked to nod or give a hand signal when he hears each new tone. Most testers use the interrupter switch at intervals during the screening, particularly when responses are uncertain or inconsistent. The left ear is tested in a like manner.

A child who hears each tone with the intensity dial at 15 decibels is considered to have normal hearing. Those who fail to hear two or

---

[12] Clarence D. O'Connor and Alice Streng, "Teaching the Acoustically Handicapped," in *The Education of Exceptional Children,* Forty-ninth Yearbook of the National Society for the Study of Education, Part II (Chicago: University of Chicago Press, 1950), p. 159. Quoted by permission of the Society.

more tones are recalled for a retest. At this time the sound at each pitch level is increased in intensity until the child can hear it, or to the maximum intensity possible. A loss of 15 decibels or more in two or more tones on a retest indicates a significant hearing impairment.[13]

It is reported that the per capita time spent in making individual screening tests with the pure-tone audiometer is no greater than in screening with the phonograph audiometer. The scoring of tests and the setting up of equipment

TABLE 4
DEGREE OF HEARING LOSS OF ALL PATIENTS ON ADMISSION TO CLINIC. BINAURAL PURE-TONE AUDIOMETER READINGS AT SCHOOL SCREENING OR FIRST CLINIC VISIT

| Degree of Loss | Audiometry, Both Ears | | Number of Cases | Percentage of 980 Cases with Known Degrees of Loss |
	Number of Tones Abnormal	Decibel Loss, Each Tone		
All degrees ..	0-18	0-110	995	100.0
Normal or very mild..	0 or 1	20 or more	110	11.2
Mild	2 or more	20 or more	578	59.0
Moderate ...	4 or more	30 or more	218	22.2
Severe	6 or more	40 or more	47	4.8
Extreme	8 or more	50 or more	17	2.8
Unknown ...	Reading not obtained, not recorded, or not satisfactory			

SOURCE: Charles R. Hayman, Benjamin S. Rich, and Eleanor Stark, "A Conservation of Hearing Program for School Children," *American Journal of Public Health*, XLI (1951), 1511.

which are required in preparing to give the phonograph audiometer test are avoided when the pure-tone machine is used.

A description of hearing impairment associated with the amount of decibel loss is suggested in Table 4.

[13] National Education Association and American Medical Association, Joint Committee on Health Problems in Education, *School Health Services*, ed. Charles C. Wilson (Washington, D. C.: National Education Association, and Chicago: American Medical Association, 1953), pp. 94-95.

Referral and Follow-up

Screening tests are not diagnostic, and when a hearing loss is discovered, there is no justification for an assumption that the child has a permanent hearing difficulty. It is entirely possible that in some instances the child's difficulty will respond to medical care and that his hearing loss will prove to be only temporary.

Precautions should be taken in the use of findings that result from screening tests for vision or hearing. In every case in which the child fails to pass the first test, all details of the testing technique should be carefully checked before a retest is given. The retest does not constitute a diagnosis, but when it confirms the original findings it does indicate with substantial accuracy which children do not meet the established standards for visual and hearing acuity. When follow-up work with parents is undertaken by nurse or teacher, it should be emphasized that only the physician is competent to diagnose hearing defects and only the licensed eye specialist is competent to diagnose vision defects.

Reports about the findings of school health department vision and hearing tests should be made by personal contact between nurse or teacher and parent. This is necessary because the report involves explanation of the testing program carried on by the school and advice about seeking professional care for the child. In follow-up relationships with parents the purpose of the contact, which is to obtain diagnosis and care for vision or hearing loss, should be kept clearly in mind. The representative of the school is not criticizing a member of the family, but is proffering professional guidance. Wisdom and skill in human relationships are called for.

Recommendations the physician may make concerning modifications of the pupil's school program are conveyed to the teacher in writing and through a nurse-teacher conference concerning the child's difficulty. With the authority of official recommendation, the teacher may then change the program of the child and will cooperate in other ways which are necessary to make his school adjustment successful.

SELECTED REFERENCES

VISION

HATHAWAY, WINIFRED. *Education and Health of the Partially Seeing Child,* 3d ed. New York: Columbia University Press, 1954.

NATIONAL SOCIETY FOR THE PREVENTION OF BLINDNESS. *Classroom Lighting.* (Publication No. 498.) New York: The Society, 1950.

———. *Eye Health.* (Publication No. 447.) New York: The Society, 1947.

———. *An Eye Health Program for Schools.* (Publication No. 141.) New York: The Society, 1951.

———. *A Guide for Eye Inspection and Testing Visual Acuity.* (Publication No. 180.) New York: The Society, 1952.

———. *"Screening," Eye Examinations, and Follow-up.* (Publication No. 443.) New York: The Society, 1945.

SHAFFER, THOMAS E. "Study of Vision Testing Procedures," *American Journal of Public Health,* XXXVIII (August, 1948), 1141-46.

HEARING

DAVIS, HALLOWELL (ed.). *Hearing and Deafness: A Guide for Laymen.* New York: Rinehart & Co., Inc., 1947.

FOWLER, EDMUND P. "Conservation of Hearing in the Schools. What Has Been Done, and What Now Should and Should Not Be Done," *Journal of School Health,* XXIV (April, 1954), 95-106.

GARDNER, W. H. "Report of Committee on Hard of Hearing Children— American Hearing Society," *Hearing News,* XVIII (February, 1950), 5-8; (March, 1950), 8-14; (April, 1950), 6-9 ff.; (May, 1950), 8-11 ff.

HARDY, WILLIAM G. *Children with Impaired Hearing, An Audiologic Perspective.* (Publication of the U. S. Children's Bureau, Bulletin No. 326.) Washington, D. C.: Government Printing Office, 1952.

HAYMAN, CHARLES R., RICH, BENJAMIN S., and STARK, ELEANOR. "A Conservation of Hearing Program for School Children," *American Journal of Public Health,* XLI (December, 1951), 1509-20.

YANKAUER, ALFRED, GEYER, MARGARET L., and CHASE, HELEN C. "Comparative Evaluation of Three Screening Methods for Detection of Hearing Loss in School Children," *American Journal of Public Health,* XLIV (January, 1954), 77-82.

Chapter 5

CONTROL OF THE COMMON COMMUNICABLE DISEASES OF CHILDREN

THE OCCURRENCE of epidemics of childhood communicable diseases in the United States has been markedly reduced during the last fifty years. We no longer have large numbers of the child population victims of diseases such as diphtheria, and we no longer have the resulting high death rates. The reduction in death rates for communicable disease has been an important factor in lowering the rate for childhood mortality from all causes. An inspection of Figure 9 indicates the magnitude of this reduction in childhood mortality during the first half of the present century. In order to gain an understanding of how advances in the control of childhood communicable disease were brought about, a knowledge of the causes of communicable disease and the methods of prevention is necessary.

Transmission of Communicable Disease

Every communicable disease has a living organism as its cause. These organisms are usually microscopic and are referred to as *micro-organisms*. Diphtheria is caused by a bacillus known as Corynebacterium diphtheria; measles, by a specific filtrable virus; and scarlet fever, by a hemolytic

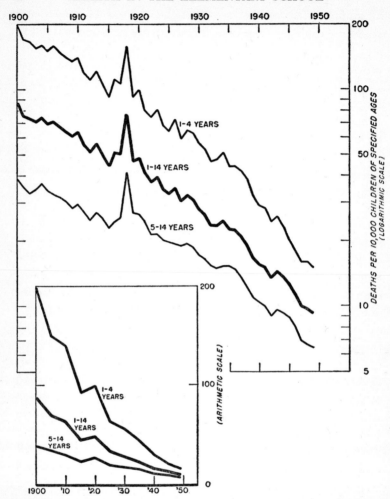

FIGURE 9. Childhood Mortality, 1900-1949 (U. S. Death Registration Area). Source: *Statistical Series No. 9* (U. S. Children's Bureau Publication [Washington, D. C., 1951]), p. 15.

streptococcus—all are examples of childhood communicable diseases produced by specific micro-organisms.

The effect on the human organism of these and other pathogenic micro-organisms may be modified by a number of factors. The extent to which the individual comes into contact with other persons who harbor the germ, the number and the virulence of the micro-organisms to which he is exposed, and his resistance to the specific micro-organism are all important factors in the problem of avoiding a communicable disease.

Certain conditions must exist for a child to catch a childhood communicable disease. In the first place there must be a source from which come the micro-organisms causing the disease. This condition is met in school whenever a child is present who is capable of transmitting the pathogenic micro-organisms he harbors to another child. The second condition is met whenever a child is present who is susceptible to the disease caused by the pathogenic micro-organisms transmitted by the first child. A child is susceptible when he has not had the disease, when he has not been immunized against it, or when he has lost immunity previously acquired. The third condition is met when a way exists for the micro-organism to get from the first child to the susceptible child. This occurs when the micro-organisms causing disease are present in the classroom and find their way to the tissues of the susceptible child. The transmission of micro-organisms from one child to another takes place when an act, such as careless sneezing or coughing, by an infected child projects discharges into the air of the classroom. The air, which suspends the discharges for a short time, acts as the agent in the transmission of micro-organisms from the tissues of the infected child to the tissues of a susceptible child.

These conditions (see Fig. 10) are illustrated by the "Chain of Infection" described in a lecture by H. H. Walker:

The "links" in the "chain" are nothing more than a series of required sets of conditions, arranged in successive steps, which must all be fulfilled before a communicable disease can pass from one person to another. The set of conditions and their order of occurrence are the same in principle for all communicable diseases, but the steps which will be most effective in preventing and controlling communicable diseases differ with each disease considered. The differences arise from the nature of the specific organism which produces a specific disease. Consequently, spread of some disease can be better prevented by breaking the early links in the chain; some by breaking the middle links; and some by breaking the links at the end.[1]

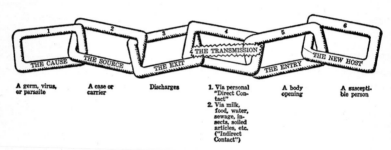

| A germ, virus, or parasite | A case or carrier | Discharges | 1. Via personal "Direct Contact"
2. Via milk, food, water, sewage, insects, soiled articles, etc. ("Indirect Contact") | A body opening | A susceptible person |

FIGURE 10. The "Chain of Infection." Source: A lecture by H. H. Walker, as quoted in Tennessee Department of Education and Tennessee Department of Public Health, *Health Teaching, A Guide for Grades 1 Through 12* (Nashville: Tennessee Department of Education and Tennessee Department of Public Health, 1953), p. 71.

When pathogenic micro-organisms reach the tissues of a susceptible child, the period of incubation begins. This is the period between the time when the susceptible child becomes host to the germ and the time when signs appear which give evidence that he has caught the disease. The incubation period varies for different diseases and also varies from person to person in those who are coming down with the same disease.

The signs of communicable disease take different forms for different diseases. Some of the more common are sore

[1] As quoted in Tennessee Department of Education and Tennessee Department of Public Health, *Health Teaching, A Guide for Grades 1 Through 12* (Nashville: Tennessee Department of Education and Tennessee Department of Public Health, 1953), p. 71. Originally published in *The Colleges of Tennessee Unite to Plan Teacher Preparation on Health Education Dedicated to Improving the Health of the People* (Nashville: Tennessee Department of Education, 1948), p. 17.

throat, headache, fever, and loss of appetite. More information about the length of the incubation period for different diseases and the signs of different diseases may be obtained from communicable disease charts issued by local departments of health or by state departments of health. In some instances, these charts will give additional information. Some include the length of exclusion periods and regulations concerning other school children in the family. This information is of value to the classroom teacher in her responsibility for cooperating in procedures designed to control childhood communicable disease (see Fig. 11).

Methods of Control

Two general methods of control are recommended in the problem of childhood communicable disease, and both are used in school health programs.

Isolation and Quarantine

The first method of control requires detection by parents and school personnel of the early signs of communicable disease and provision for isolation of the child until he is no longer capable of transmitting the germs causing his illness to a susceptible individual. With accompanying restrictions on the activity of others with whom the ill child has been in contact and who in turn may become carriers, this method of control has been in use a long time. On the whole, it is not a very satisfactory method. We cannot be certain of isolating the victim of a communicable disease as soon as he becomes capable of transmitting it to another person, and because regulations aimed at restricting the activities of individuals are difficult to enforce, it is clear that isolation and quarantine cannot be highly successful as preventive measures.

REPORTABLE DISEASE CHART—SCHOOL GUIDE
GREATER HARTFORD HEALTH AREA

DISEASE	PUPIL WITH DISEASE		CONTACTS FAMILY AND SCHOOL	REMARKS
	EXCLUDED FROM SCHOOL	READMITTED ON	PERIOD OF INSPECTION AT SCHOOL BY NURSE, TEACHER OR PHYSICIAN	Any contact with any of the following signs or symptoms should be examined further before admission to school.
Chickenpox	Until all *Primary* scabs have come off — not longer than 6 days	School Inspection	None	Abdominal pain
German Measles	For 7 days from onset of catarrhal symptoms	School Inspection	None	Body ache
Measles	For 5 days from time rash appeared	School Inspection	daily for 10 days	Chills Coughs Diarrhea Fever
Mumps	As long as the glands remain swollen	School Inspection	None	Headache Loss of appetite Malaise (logy feeling)
Poliomyelitis (Infantile Paralysis)	A minimum of 2 weeks from onset of disease	School Inspection	daily for 14 days from last contact	Rash Signs of a cold
Ringworm of Scalp	Unless under treatment	School Inspection	Regular intervals with filtered ultra violet	Sore Throat Watering of eyes
Scarlet fever and all Streptococcal Infections of the upper respiratory tract	For 7 days from onset of 1st symptoms — sore throat or rash	School Inspection	daily for 5 days from date of last contact	(OVER)

70

(Face of card)

CASES WHERE CONTACTS ARE EXCLUDED FROM SCHOOL

DISEASE	PUPIL WITH DISEASE		FAMILY and SCHOOL CONTACTS	REMARKS
	EXCLUDED FROM SCHOOL	READMITTED ON	BASIS OF RE-ADMISSION OF SCHOOL CHILDREN	
Diphtheria (Cases and Carriers)	Until 2 successive negative cultures taken not less than 24 hours apart are negative.	Card From Health Department	Not admitted until 2 successive negative nose and throat cultures, taken not less than 24 hours apart are done.	In cases where cultures are persistently positive in absence of recognizable disease—virulence tests will be done.
Smallpox	Until all scabs and crusts have disappeared.	Card From Health Department	Excluded for 16 days from last exposure. Contacts admitted only on card from Health Department.	It will be recommended that all contacts be vaccinated immediately after exposure.
Whooping Cough	For 3 weeks after a typical "whoop" has been established.	Card From Health Department	Isolation of non-immunes at home for 14 days after last exposure	Not all cases have typical "whoops". A typical case lasts from one to two months.

CERTAIN OTHER DISEASES OF PUBLIC HEALTH SIGNIFICANCE

	CONTROL MEASURES	SUGGESTED PROCEDURES
Impetigo	Permit pupils to remain in school if lesions are covered. Check contacts.	Soak off crusts and apply medication prescribed by physician.
Pediculosis	Exclude from school until treatment has been inaugurated. Check contacts and advise treatment if indicated. Inspect Daily. Instruct parents in the application of 10% DDT in talc.	In instances where parents will not, or cannot, carry out DDT treatment, the treatment may be given by school nurse, providing she first obtains written permission of parents.
Scabies	Exclude from School. Check contacts.	See family physician.

NOTE: All duly licensed physicians and school nurses shall be considered authorized agents of the local health officer for the purposes of re-admission to school.

(*Reverse side*)

FIGURE 11. Communicable Disease Chart. Source: Board of Health, Hartford, Conn.

There is a substantial body of opinion which holds that it is better for most children to catch the common childhood communicable diseases, such as measles, chicken pox, and mumps, and as a consequence to acquire immunity which lasts for a long time, if not for life. If such a plan is followed, medical guidance is necessary and unnecessary exposure is not advocated. This point of view will be discussed later.

Immunity

The second method of control involves the use of immunizing techniques which, if successful, result in the individual's becoming immune to the disease for which he has been given preventive treatment. An individual may get immunity by a number of different methods. In considering the elementary school child and the more common childhood communicable diseases, we are concerned with acquired immunity which results when:

1. The child has had the disease. An attack of measles or mumps, for example, usually confers long-lasting immunity.

2. The child becomes host to the organism causing a specific disease and develops immunity, although clinical signs of the disease do not develop. There are some individuals who seem by virtue of constitutional traits to possess a higher degree of resistance to pathogenic organisms than others. To illustrate, before immunizing against diphtheria became a general practice, there were many instances in which the pathogenic micro-organism causing diphtheria did not produce characteristic symptoms of the infection (no record of the individual's having had the disease), but the individual had acquired resistance to the disease.

3. The child is immunized artificially. This procedure results in passive or in active immunity. Passive immunity is acquired when a child receives an injection of material which already contains antibodies, as diphtheria anti-

toxin. The immunity acquired in this way is of short duration. Active immunity results when an antigen, such as diphtheria toxoid, is used in the immunizing procedure. The tissues of the body are stimulated to produce antibodies, and although the resulting immunity develops more slowly, it is more lasting. Diphtheria, which was formerly a serious childhood communicable disease problem, is no longer a menace when proper preventive measures are taken by child health authorities. The excellent work carried on by Schick, Park, and others about 1913 has resulted in a marked reduction in mortality from diphtheria. We do not have the many individuals who are handicapped throughout life by permanent damage to the heart and to other body tissues as a possible result of diphtheria. As a matter of fact, there is no reason why a child should have diphtheria today. The private physician, the official and voluntary health agencies, and the school health department all urge that children be immunized against diphtheria, and in most instances, make such treatment easily available.

The same assurance of immunity achieved by the preventive measures for diphtheria has not yet been achieved for other common childhood diseases. For example, although a form of preventive treatment for measles is available, usually the primary purpose of the treatment is to reduce the severity of the attack. The less severe attack, however, does produce active immunity. Gamma globulin, used in preventing or modifying an attack of measles, is not a vaccine; it is a fraction of human blood which contains antibodies that render the individual capable of resisting an attack of measles. The source of immune serum globulin is human whole blood. Most human beings have had measles and have developed an active immunity against the disease. When used to treat a susceptible individual, the fraction of their blood, which contains antibodies, is effective in preventing or reducing the severity of the disease.

As time goes on, we may reasonably expect that further technical advances in the control of childhood communicable disease will be made and that preventive treatments in the form of vaccines that produce active immunity will be available for other childhood diseases for which we have inadequate protection at present.

Newer concepts suggest a changing emphasis in procedures for the control of certain childhood communicable diseases. In the main, this emphasis is on reducing restrictions which for many years have been recommended as measures for controlling childhood communicable disease. A statement which indicates this trend appears in The Report of the Third National Conference of Physicians and Schools:

> In certain communities where the apparent advantages of exposure of children of elementary school age to German measles, chicken pox and mumps is well understood and where there is agreement among parents, physicians, and school and public health personnel, deliberate exposure under control conditions may be encouraged. This procedure is based on the premise that all people who have not had German measles, chicken pox, or mumps are susceptible to them, and that these diseases are less severe and less hazardous between the ages of 5 and 10 years.
>
> Communicable disease regulations as set forth by state and local health agencies should govern in all cases. The trend is toward reducing restrictions on the basis that restrictions alone do not control this group of diseases. Their special hazards to infants, children of preschool age, children who are not well, and pregnant women who have not had them, must be kept in mind.[2]

Responsibility for Control

Responsibility for the control of childhood communicable disease rests not only with the official health agency, but also with the home and the school. A completely effective program of prevention can be carried on only when there is

[2] *Physicians and Schools.* (Chicago: American Medical Association, 1952), p. 45.

a substantial understanding of the problem by these three groups and a high degree of cooperation among them.

Parents should be informed by the school authorities and by the official health department about the early signs of childhood communicable disease, and should be urged to keep children at home whenever a suspicious condition arises. If the child is coming down with a communicable disease, he is better off at home than in school. In addition, other children are protected from him. In event a child becomes ill while at school, the responsibility of the school is to administer first-aid and to arrange for the child to be taken home (see Chap. 6).

There is a possibility that articles with which the infected child has come into contact, as books and classroom furniture, are instrumental in the transmission of disease. We know that factors in the transmission of communicable disease in the classroom are an infected child, a susceptible child, and a means of transmitting the infection from the first to the second child. If the school health department is to utilize all means for controlling the spread of infection, articles with which the infected child has recently been in contact should be taken out of circulation and handled in accordance with local or state health department regulations. The desk, chairs, and other furniture may be washed with a strong soap and water solution. Usually these procedures are followed only for the major communicable diseases and are not followed for the less serious diseases.

The general responsibility within the school for the control of childhood communicable disease lies with the physician and the nurse, who work as members of a school health service staff, but they rely heavily on the skill and the cooperation of the classroom teacher. This is true regardless of whether the physician and the nurse are members of a staff responsible to the board of education or responsible to the board of health. The classroom teacher is in a better position than any other school employee for continued daily observation of children in her classroom. The teacher has twenty to forty or more pupils in her classroom; the number of pupils for which the nurse is usually responsible may range from a few hundred to fifteen hundred or more; in most schools the amount of physician service available is less than the amount of nursing service. Under these conditions, continued individual observation and care of pupils by the health specialists are impossible. Because of the smaller number of pupils with which she deals and because of her direct and daily contact with them, the teacher becomes the key person in maintaining high standards of health welfare in her classroom.

Regardless of changed emphasis on certain aspects of childhood communicable disease control, the teacher has a definite responsibility for determining whether a school child shows signs of present or oncoming illness. The classroom teacher is neither qualified nor expected to perform the functions of the school nurse. However, as a result of pre-service and in-service training and experience, she should be able to detect deviations from normal appearance and behavior of individual children in her class. The generally accepted practice for the purpose of noting such deviations is continuous observation of pupils (see Chap. 3). The teacher's function is not to diagnose but (1) to be aware of the child who is giving evidence of other than normal appearance or behavior, and (2) to get him away from the group and into the hands of the health specialist who then assumes responsibility for him. The child who shows any signs or symptoms of a childhood communicable disease does not belong in school. It is possible that a "running" nose may be due to a cold only, but this condition is also one of the early indications of other communicable diseases, such as measles. In either case, and for his own good at least, the child should be at home and under proper care. When a health specialist is not available, a teacher or school administrator has the responsibility for making arrangements, preferably with the parents, to get the child home.

Regulations for Control

The regulations governing exclusion and readmission to school after illness are established by the local board of health, which has legal responsibility for the control of communicable disease. In situations where the school health program is administered by the board of education, these regulations for exclusion and for the readmission of children after illness are carried out by school people. The basic consideration in readmission is whether the returning child will be a hazard to other pupils. Readmission to school is usually permitted on the basis of established regulation or on the opinion of the health officer, school physician, family physician, or school nurse. In cases of the more serious communicable diseases, such as poliomyelitis, meningococcus meningitis, and diphtheria, readmission is granted by the health officer only. In other cases (mumps and chicken pox, for example) the nurse may make the decision. However, in many instances the services of a health specialist are not available for decisions about readmission. Then the school principal or the classroom teacher makes the decision. As a guide for such decisions, the regulations of the local or the state department of health serve to determine the period of exclusion from school and the readmission of pupils to school after illness (see Fig. 11).

There seems to be a tendency toward modifying the regulations requiring the exclusion of pupils who have been exposed to certain childhood communicable diseases, such as measles, mumps, and chicken pox. In some parts of the country, contacts are permitted to stay in school. This practice seems to reflect the opinion that some of the former practices of exclusion and readmission have not been particularly effective.

Local health authorities, the school board, and the school administrator have the responsibility of deciding whether to close schools in the event of an increasing number of cases of communicable disease. In this problem the legal responsibility rests with the department of health. The question is one of deciding what action, if any, will reduce the incidence of cases. The established factors in the transmission of communicable disease suggest the answer to this question. The action should result in a reduction in the number of contacts among school children. If closing of the schools will do that, then the course to be followed is clear. But in urban areas the school is only one of a number of places where children have group contacts. Unless all other contacts (possible at movie houses, at playgrounds, and through group activities) are prohibited, closing of the schools in urban areas does not reduce contacts among school pupils to the point of being effective. A commonly recommended practice is to keep schools open, and when the children arrive at school, to conduct a careful inspection by physician, nurse, and teacher. For suspects, the standard isolation and exclusion procedure (referred to earlier in this chapter) is then followed. Cooperation of parents, gained through previous contacts between school nurse and home and between teacher and home, is particularly useful in this situation. An alert and informed parent keeps a child at home when the child shows signs of communicable disease.

In a rural situation, closing of the schools may effectively reduce contacts between children. The usual school contacts and the close contacts that result from bus transportation are eliminated. If parents are informed and their cooperation gained, other group contacts which are part of community living can be reduced or temporarily eliminated until the danger has passed.

In reference to the opening of schools after a vacation period, the same principle as mentioned above is used to determine the course of action. Until the danger has passed, postponing the reopening of schools reduces to some extent the number of contacts among children. When schools have been closed by action of health authorities and education authorities or where reopening after a vacation period has been postponed, the local health authority recommends when the schools may be opened.

Common Skin Infections

Impetigo

Some of the relatively minor infections of children can be a source of trouble and concern to the classroom teacher. For example, some children have annoying skin infections when they return to school after a prolonged vacation. Although infections of this kind may occur at any time, more of them seem to occur at the opening of school after the summer vacation. Impetigo, which is probably caused by a staphylococcal or a streptococcal infection and to which children are particularly susceptible, is commonly found on face and hands but sometimes is present on other parts of the body. This infection appears in the form of blisters which subsequently develop into crusted areas, yellow or brown in appearance. In an attempt to relieve the itching that accompanies this infection, a child may scratch the lesions, and in so doing, may transmit the infection to some part of his body or to another child who handles articles that have been used by the infected child. Medical attention is recommended for a child infected with impetigo.

In some school systems the school health department is instrumental through its nursing service in recommending specific curative procedure to parents. In some instances an infected child is excluded from school until the lesion has healed (not a long time when the child is under proper treatment). In others the child is permitted to stay in school under conditions that insure no direct or indirect contact between an uninfected child and the lesions of an infected child.

Ringworm

Although there are different forms of ringworm, the one which most concerns elementary school teachers and health specialists is ringworm of the scalp. In this condition the child is infected by a microscopic human-type fungus which prefers the human scalp for its growth. This infection is described as one in which round patches, which are scaly and gray in color and have short broken-off hairs, are present on the scalp. This type of ringworm spreads rapidly from person to person and is very difficult to control. The source of infection is both direct, by person-to-person contact, and indirect, by contact with clothing, or surfaces with which the head comes into contact, or articles such as clippers which a barber has used on an infected person. An infected person may transmit the infection just as long as fungi and their spores are present at the infected area. The transmission is very easy because even on one piece of hair in the infected region there are large numbers of fungi and spores. In view of the ease of transmission and the difficulty of control, the infected child should be immediately placed under medical care. All children are susceptible. A child does not develop immunity to ringworm, and reinfection is common. The exact precautions which should be taken against transmission depend on the recommendations of the local health authorities, but basic to all control is avoidance of direct and indirect contact between the infected child and others. This means exclusion of the child from school until the fungi and the spores are no longer present on his scalp.

The classroom teacher and the nurse should be alert to the appearance of conditions which may be ringworm of the scalp. It is not readily detected in its early stages unless the scalp is observed under filtered ultraviolet light. The teacher can encourage cleanliness of the scalp and the hair and can discourage the common use of combs and brushes and the exchange of headgear by children. These are recognized preventive techniques.

Scabies

Occasionally, a teacher has a child in her classroom who shows signs of having an infestation with scabies, commonly referred to as "the itch." The cause of this troublesome condition is a small burrowing mite which gets into the skin and then lays her eggs there. The result is small blisters with a thin black center. The burrows of the mite are commonly found in the skin of hands, wrists, armpits, abdomen, and undersides of thighs. The infested child is troubled at night by itching of the affected areas. He is a hazard to other children with whom he may come into contact and should be excluded from school until he is no longer infested. Under proper care, scabies can be cured without much difficulty. The school nurse or the public health nurse can be instrumental in helping the child and the parents to remedy the condition. She can also be instrumental in preventing the spread of the infestation to other members of the family by recommending avoidance of common use of towels, clothing, and bedding.

Pediculosis

The most common form of pediculosis among school children is caused by the head louse. Like scabies, it is a condition that is usually referred to as an infestation. The source of the infestation is another person or his personal belongings. The infested child can transmit pediculosis just as long

82   HEALTH IN THE ELEMENTARY SCHOOL

as he harbors live lice or their eggs (nits). The eggs of the louse are found very close to the scalp and may be seen as small dark lumps attached to the hair. The ordinary playful activity of school children on the way to and from school and on the playground encourages the transmission of head lice from an infested child to other children. Transmission is also possible when an infested child's clothing comes into contact with clothing of other children.

The problem of control hinges on continuous observation by the teacher, who should be particularly suspicious of a child who persistently scratches his head. Live pediculi are controlled by the use of an effective insecticide which is applied to scalp, skin, and clothing of an infested child. The incubation period of the larva is about one week to ten days. At the end of this period a second treatment with insecticide may be required.

SELECTED REFERENCES

AMERICAN PUBLIC HEALTH ASSOCIATION. *The Control of Communicable Diseases in Man,* 7th ed. New York: The Association, 1950.
ANDERSON, GAYLORD W., and ARNSTEIN, MARGARET G. *Communicable Disease Control,* 3d ed. New York: The Macmillan Co., 1953.
METROPOLITAN LIFE INSURANCE COMPANY. "Host Resistance," *Health Bulletin for Teachers,* XVIII (April, 1947), 9-12.
———. "Parasite Resistance," *Health Bulletin for Teachers,* XVIII (March, 1947), 5-8.
MUSTARD, HARRY S. *An Introduction to Public Health,* 3d ed. New York: The Macmillan Co., 1953.
RAWLINGS, JUNIUS M., M.D. "Relation of Nutrition to Infection in Children," *American Journal of Public Health,* XXXIX (July, 1949), 858-61.
SALK, JONAS, *et al.* "Studies in Human Subjects on Active Immunization Against Poliomyelitis," *American Journal of Public Health,* XLIV (August, 1954), 994-1009.
SALLE, A. J. *Fundamental Principles of Bacteriology,* 4th ed. New York: McGraw-Hill Book Co., Inc., 1954.
WILSON, CHARLES C.(ed.). *School Health Services.* Report of the Joint Committee on Health Problems in Education of the National Education Association and the American Medical Association. Washington, D. C.: National Education Association, and Chicago: American Medical Association, 1953, pp. 269-303.

Chapter 6

EMERGENCY CARE IN ACCIDENTS
AND SUDDEN ILLNESS

THERE ARE occasions with any group of children of elementary school age when, due to accident or sudden illness, need arises for emergency care. These situations develop in spite of the best in safety education and practices, and in spite of all precautions taken by school and home to prevent illness. The elementary school child is active and enjoys big-muscle activity encouraged by the games program of the school, with the result that injuries do occur from time to time. The majority of school accidents arise from this cause and are not serious. The most common cases of illness for which emergency care is required in school are stomach upsets, fainting, cuts, bruises, and similar types of difficulty. Serious injuries and illnesses of school children while in school make up only a small percentage of accident and illness cases.

Responsibility

Regardless of whether or not the illness or injury is serious, the school has a responsibility for emergency care.

The most commonly accepted principle governing the function of the school in relation to sudden illness and accidental injury is that it is responsible for the *emergency* handling of these situations but is not responsible for subsequent treatment. The school provides facili-

83

ties and the personnel with proper training to act promptly and intelligently in emergencies for the saving of life, the prevention of further injury, and the alleviation of pain as far as this can be done by nonmedical persons.[1]

When nursing service is immediately available, accidents and cases of sudden illness are referred to the school nurse. In the larger school systems well-staffed with medical and nursing personnel, a physician or nurse may be on call for the more serious emergencies if neither is present at the school when the accident or illness occurs. When nursing service is not available, some schools have followed the practice of delegating the responsibility for first-aid work to one member of the school staff. It is considered more desirable, however, to have several members of the staff qualified in first-aid procedures and available for this assignment.

In every case requiring emergency care, the immediate responsibility rests with the classroom teacher. In carrying out this responsibility she needs to understand the established school practices in emergency care and the specific procedure required for different situations. The teacher is in charge of the emergency until responsibility for the child is assumed by some other member of the school staff, the school nurse, the school or family physician, the child's parents, or other responsible person.

The teacher should not overstep the limits of her responsibility by attempting to diagnose, nor should she administer any kind of medication. The responsibility of the school in the matter of emergency care does not extend beyond the procedures usually recognized as appropriate for first-aid treatment.

Although the majority of school accidents are classified as minor, an established procedure is necessary for taking care

---

[1] Commission on Health in Schools, *Health in Schools,* Twentieth Yearbook of the American Association of School Administrators (rev. ed.; Washington, D. C.: National Education Association, 1951), p. 385.

of them and of others of a more serious nature which may occur. This requires planning if emergencies are to be handled effectively. All plans for emergency care should be approved by the school principal. The responsibility for preparing these plans might be assigned to the school physician, the nurse, or a committee appointed for this purpose. Such plans—in writing and placed in the hands of all members of the school staff—become standing orders and guides for the efficient care of emergencies. The person or persons responsible for emergency care should be assigned and a specific location designated for an emergency room.

Procedures

The actual first-aid procedures followed by the person in charge are outlined in detail for specific types of emergencies. The procedures to be followed for obtaining medical care quickly and for obtaining ambulance service in the more serious emergencies should be stated. If the school physician or the child's family physician is not available, instructions for obtaining the services of the nearest available physician should be given.

In the less serious cases, after immediate first-aid care has been given, there may be need for taking the child home. In the compact community this may not be a serious problem, but even in this situation the child should be accompanied by an adult, and the responsibility of this adult does not end until he has delivered the child into competent hands. This individual representing the school should be qualified to make recommendations to a parent concerning medical care or to suggest ways of obtaining community agency services. In rural situations the problem becomes difficult, but the same principles of responsibility apply as in the more compact communities. Planning by school authorities and by representatives of parent groups is required to work out the details for getting the child home or under the care of a properly delegated person.

In every case of serious illness or injury at school, the home should be notified immediately and the wishes of parents should be followed when medical care or hospitalization is necessary. The actual arrangements for medical care or hospitalization should be made by the parent of the ill or injured child when it is possible for the parent to do so. This aspect of the emergency care program is usually dealt with by board of education regulations which concern the legal and policy considerations of the problem. Such regulations are incorporated in the standing orders. Some schools follow the very admirable plan of having on file for emergency use the names of a second or third responsible person whom the schools may notify in event the parents of a child cannot be reached immediately.

Actually, serious illness of an elementary school child while he is in school is not a common occurrence, and when this does happen, the classroom teacher is neither competent nor authorized to diagnose the condition. She notes evidence of severe pain, fainting, fever, and markedly unusual behavior and immediately takes measures to obtain emergency medical care for the child. In the meantime the child should be kept warm, quiet, and preferably in a horizontal position. The more common illnesses that manifest themselves as aches, such as earache, headache, toothache, and stomach-ache, are not to be dismissed lightly. Ordinarily, these do not call for emergency action, but good school-home cooperation in child health care requires that the home be informed of the complaint which the child made while he was in school.

The majority of accidents to elementary school children while in school result in skin abrasions and cuts which require standard first-aid care. The teacher may or may not take responsibility for this work. Whether she does or does not depends on the policy adopted by the particular school. The more serious accidents, which occur occasionally, may result in excessive bleeding, unconsciousness, bone fracture. Under these conditions, the teacher should follow standard first-aid procedures and immediately call for medical aid.

First-Aid Supplies

Although first-aid supplies are kept in the room designated for emergency care, they should be available to every teacher who may wish to use them. The kind and the quantity of supplies with which this room is stocked are determined with the caution in mind that first-aid work only is to be done. If the school is served by a physician or a nurse, the stocking of the emergency room becomes the responsibility of this health specialist. Table 5 lists supplies that have been suggested as suitable for the school first-aid room.

TABLE 5
First-Aid Supplies and How to Use Them

Suggested Supplies	What They Are For
Tincture of green soap	Washing injured parts
Hospital cotton, roll	Large soft pads or dressings
Absorbent cotton, sterilized, roll, box or "picking" package	Swabs or pledgets for applying medication or wiping wounds
Dressings, large or small pads, sterilized, in individual transparent envelopes	For protecting injuries
Dressings, finger, in envelopes	For protecting very small injuries
Adhesive tape, roll, one inch	Fastening dressings, or splints
Scissors, bandage or blunt	Cutting dressings
Toothpicks	For making swabs
Alcohol, 70% (water 30%), or rubbing alcohol	Disinfecting skin and minor wounds
Mercurochrome, 2% aqueous	Minor injuries, especially in young children
Other disinfectant, if ordered by physician	As ordered by physician
Mineral oil, bottle, or petroleum jelly, tube or jar, white or yellow, but not medicated	For removing ointments; in eye to relieve irritation from foreign body; for burns if no other ointment is at hand

TABLE 5 (*continued*)

Suggested Supplies	What They Are For
Boric acid ointment U.S.P.	For very small minor first degree burns only
Epsom salts	In hot water, a handful to a basin, for soaking sprains, bruises, or infection when ordered by a physician
Baking soda, powder	Teaspoonful to a pint of warm watei for mouthwash, or gargle if ordered
Salt, crystal or tablets	Same as baking soda, or with baking soda, as directed
Hot-water bottle with cover	Local relief of pain
Ice bag	Local relief of pain
Two warm blankets	For prevention of chilling
Tourniquet (three feet of soft rubber tubing and a stick or pencil)	Use ABOVE place from where red blood spurts. Call doctor at once. Release every 15 minutes to allow circulation to reach parts, then reapply if necessary
Eye droppers	Dropping liquid medicines
Ear syringe, soft rubber	For ears only when ordered by physician
Graduated medicine glass*	For measuring liquid medicines
Drugs for internal use	Only when ordered by physician and as directed by him

Prepared by the American Medical Association.

* A graduated medicine glass is most accurate and should be used whenever possible. In emergency, this table may be used:

```
20 drops (water solution)  ...................   1 cc. (metric)
1 teaspoon (measuring spoon, not table silver) ....   5 cc.
1 tablespoon (measuring spoon, not table silver) ..  15 cc.
1 wineglass  .............................   50 cc.
1 tumbler  ................................  250 cc.
```

Source: Commission on Health in Schools, *Health in Schools*, Twentieth Yearbook of the American Association of School Administrators (rev. ed.; Washington, D. C.: National Education Association, 1951), pp. 394-95.

In addition to suggestions about the use of first-aid supplies, a manual of procedures which the teacher can follow in specific types of accidents and sudden illness should be available. The Red Cross First-Aid Textbook or specific instructions recommended by the school health department may be used as a manual.

Although many of the illnesses are not common, the kinds of illness which may beset elementary school children have been listed in *Suggested School Health Policies, A Charter for School Health:*

Communicable diseases vary in incidence and importance in different localities. Among the communicable diseases with which a school might have to contend are: Amebic dysentery, bacillary dysentery, botulism, chicken pox, common cold, diphtheria, encephalitis (sleeping sickness), food infections and food poisonings, German measles, gonorrhea, hookworm disease, impetigo contagiosa, infantile paralysis (poliomyelitis), influenza, lockjaw (tetanus), malaria, measles, meningitis, mumps, pneumonia, rabies, ringworm, scarlet fever, septic sore throat, smallpox, syphilis, trachoma, trench mouth (Vincent's infection), trichinosis, tuberculosis, tularemia, typhoid fever, typhus fever, undulant fever, and whooping cough.[2]

Teacher Liability

Each accident taking place when the child or school employee is under the jurisdiction of the school or engaged in school duties should be recorded in detail, and a report should be forwarded to the person authorized to receive such a report. Among the items which are included in an adequate report are the following:

Name, age, home address, grade in school of child injured
Day, time, and location of accident
Person in charge of child at time of accident
Description of accident
Description of injury
Names of witnesses
Immediate first-aid treatment given
Final disposition of the case

[2] National Conference for Cooperation in Health Education, National Committee on School Health Policies (2d ed.; New York: Health Education Council, 1950), p. 21.

Name of person taking over responsibility for the child
Signatures of teacher in charge and of immediate superior

Associated with the teacher's responsibility in cases of injury or sudden illness to pupils is the problem of negligence in the event her action or failure to act results in harm to the pupils.

If immediate first-aid treatment seems indicated, the teacher is obligated by his relationship to the pupil *in loco parentis* to do the best he can. Only such first-aid knowledge as is expected of laymen is required of teachers in these circumstances, but every teacher should be trained in at least the rudiments of first-aid. If the injured pupil does not need immediate attention, the teacher should await the attendance of a medically trained person rather than attempt to do something which may leave the pupil in worse condition. Failure to act or unwise action may lead to a charge of negligence against the teacher.[3]

Every individual is responsible for his own negligence. If a teacher is negligent, he is legally responsible and is subject to the payment of damages out of his own pocket except in the three states where judgments against teachers are to be paid out of school funds.[4]

The three states referred to are Connecticut, New Jersey, and New York. It is desirable for a teacher to be informed about the laws of her state that concern legal responsibility for negligence associated with her activities in emergency care.

In many instances a teacher has obtained liability insurance, sometimes under a group policy, as a form of protection against financial loss should a successful suit be brought against her. There seems to be increasing interest by school officials and parents in insurance plans which are designed to provide benefit payments to pupils who may be injured while taking part in school-sponsored activities. Arrange-

[3] National Education Association, Research Division, *Who Is Liable for Pupil Injuries?* Prepared for the National Commission on Safety Education (Washington, D. C.: National Education Association, 1950), p. 25.
[4] *Ibid.*, p. 15.

ments for pupil participation in such plans are a responsibility of the school administrator and must be approved by
the board of education. This matter usually involves legal
opinion and questions of board of education policy, because
of the financial aspects of the problem. In the states of Wisconsin and Pennsylvania, for example, accident benefit plans
have been operating for many years under the Interscholas-
tic Athletic Association of the state. In many places the
benefit insurance plans of private organizations are in use.

SELECTED REFERENCES

AMERICAN RED CROSS. *American Red Cross First-Aid Textbook,* rev. ed.
Philadelphia: P. Blakiston's Sons & Co., Inc., 1945.

COMMISSION ON HEALTH IN SCHOOLS. *Health in Schools,* rev. ed. Twentieth
Yearbook of the American Association of School Administrators. Washington, D. C.: National Education Association, 1951, pp. 385-411.

ELIASON, ELDRIDGE L. *First Aid in Emergencies,* 12th ed. Philadelphia:
J. B. Lippincott Co., 1948.

METROPOLITAN LIFE INSURANCE COMPANY. *First Aid.* New York: The
Company, 1947.

NATIONAL CONFERENCE FOR COOPERATION IN HEALTH EDUCATION, National
Committee on School Health Policies. *Suggested School Health Policies.
A Charter for School Health,* 2d ed. New York: Health Education Coun-
cil, 1950.

NATIONAL EDUCATION ASSOCIATION, Research Division. *Who Is Liable for
Pupil Injuries?* Prepared for the National Commission on Safety Education. Washington, D. C.: National Education Association, 1950.

RICHARDS, DOROTHY M. "First Aid Treatment," Unit 10 in ROTHWEILER,
ELLA, and WHITE, JEAN. *The Art and Science of Nursing,* 4th ed.
Philadelphia: F. A. Davis Co., 1949, pp. 761-847.

WILSON, CHARLES C. (ed.). *School Health Services.* Report of the Joint
Committee on Health Problems in Education of the National Education
Association and the American Medical Association. Washington, D. C.:
National Education Association, and Chicago: American Medical Asso-
ciation, 1953, pp. 229-65.

Chapter 7

THE PROGRAM FOR PHYSICALLY
HANDICAPPED CHILDREN
IN SCHOOL

Basic to constructive work with physically handicapped children is the need for early identification of these children. Unusualness in appearance or behavior calls for early referral to a physician for his opinion about a parent's or teacher's suspicion of atypicalness. If the physician confirms the suspicion that the child's variation from his normal appearance or behavior is such that medical attention is required, this attention can be given before handicapping takes place and before substantial modification in the educational program becomes necessary. If the handicap is irremediable, early identification and diagnosis make possible the kind of modified educational program adapted to the individual's limitations. Early identification of handicapped children can be furthered materially by the classroom teacher when she carries out her responsibilities for continued observation of pupils (see Chap. 3).

Extent of Problem

In every school system which serves a reasonably large population group area there are children who differ from the vast majority. In some instances these children are unable to take part in the regular class program. Special arrangements in the form of a modified school program are necessary if we are to insure adequate educational opportunity for them. The problems of the classroom teacher with handicapped children vary markedly because the number of such children in her classroom changes from year to year and because each handicapped child must have a program modified to suit his particular limitations.

An estimate of the number of exceptional children who are in need of special educational services in the elementary and the secondary schools of the United States is about four million. This estimate of four million includes children in the general groupings, as follows:

1. Children with physical handicaps

   a) Crippled children—those with poliomyelitis, cerebral palsy, congenital deformities, and other orthopedic handicaps; also children with cardiac difficulties, sometimes called "crippled hearts"

   b) Children with impaired hearing—the congenitally deaf, the adventitiously deaf, and the hard of hearing

   c) Children with visual impairments—the blind and the partially seeing

   d) Children with speech handicaps

   e) Children with other types of physical handicaps, such as tuberculosis, epilepsy, and endocrine disorders

2. Children with mental deviations

   a) Children of low intelligence, including both the feebleminded and those who are less seriously defective in intellectual development

   b) Children with high intelligence, including both those with special talents and those who are superior in general intellectual abilities

3. Children with emotional or social maladjustments, including those with serious behavior disorders or emotional disturbances[1]

The number of physically handicapped children (Group 1 above) for whom adjustments are actually made in the regular classroom cannot be accurately determined. However, that such children are present in many regular classrooms cannot be questioned, and it is with such children that we are concerned.

Present-day philosophy in regard to the education of the physically handicapped child recognizes that, in all particulars, the educational objectives are the same for him as for the normal child. He has the same basic drives and the same need for satisfactions. The physically handicapped child must develop into a well-adjusted adult and must accept the responsibilities of citizenship. His handicap may require individual arrangement of educational experiences. Such an arrangement, which calls for program adjustment or special services, is made for the purpose of providing the same educational rights as are enjoyed by the normal child. Through no fault of his own, the handicapped child must bear the penalty of his misfortune. Failure to provide equal educational opportunity for him is not in accordance with basic concepts of American education.

The extent to which the problem of the physically handicapped child is recognized at the state level of education is indicated by the fact that in 1952 some form of legislation, permissive or mandatory, was found in forty states. In thirty-seven states this legislation provides for subsidies from state school funds to the local districts for educational pro-

[1] The Yearbook Committee, "Basic Facts and Principles Underlying Special Education," in *The Education of Exceptional Children*, Forty-ninth Yearbook of the National Society for the Study of Education, Part II (Chicago: University of Chicago Press, 1950), p. 7. Quoted by permission of the Society.

grams for the physically handicapped. In forty-one states provision is made by the state department of education for supervisory or consultive services for special education, of which work with the physically handicapped is a part. In forty-one states legislation has been enacted which provides supervisory or consultive services by the department of education (see Table 6).

Teacher Responsibility for Children with Handicaps

Where medical and nursing services are available to schools, the problem of early identification of physical defects is not difficult. Screening by specialists and individual clinical appraisal by physicians are the generally used techniques (see Chap. 3). Unless this work is done by the nursing or some other specialized service, the classroom teacher conducts tests as a first procedure for screening defects of hearing and vision. She also uses the procedures of continuous observation of pupils to detect variation in appearance or behavior. Her responsibility, beyond the identification of unusual appearance or behavior, is (1) to refer the child to specialists within the school system if they are available, or (2) to inform the parents about the problem in order that they may obtain medical opinion, and if necessary, remedial care for the child. In the absence of well-organized school medical services, the responsibility for identification falls on the classroom teacher, who is limited to the simpler screening procedures. The types of deviations with which we are concerned here are those mentioned on page 93 in Group 1, "Children with physical handicaps."

Orthopedic

An orthopedic defect that is obvious is known to parents and becomes known to a teacher when the child enters

TABLE 6

THE LEGISLATIVE STATUS OF PUBLIC SCHOOL SPECIAL EDUCATION PROGRAMS FOR THE PHYSICALLY HANDICAPPED IN CONTINENTAL UNITED STATES, JUNE, 1952

State (1)	Various Handicapping Conditions Including Speech			Restricted to One or Two Types of Programs			Remarks
	Mandatory (2)	Permissive (3)	Type of reimbursement (4)	Mandatory (5)	Permissive (6)	Type of reimbursement (7)	
Alabama		xx	None				
Arizona					x	B₁	
Arkansas	x		A₃				
California		x	A₃				
Colorado		x	A₃				
Connecticut	x		A₃				
Delaware	xx		A₁				
Florida	x		B₂				
Georgia		xx	B₃				Law specifies exceptional children. Interpretation is assumed.
Idaho		xx	B₂				
Illinois		x	A₃				
Indiana		x	A₁				
Iowa		x	A₁				
Kansas		xx	None				Local districts may levy 1 mill tax to support programs of special education
Kentucky		x	A₃				
Louisiana		x	A₃				
Maine	x		A₃				
Maryland		x	D				
Massachusetts	x		A₃				
Michigan		x	A₃				

State					Remarks
Missouri	x	A_3			
Montana		A_3			No legislation
Nebraska	x				No legislation
Nevada		None			
New Hampshire	x	A_2			
New Jersey	x				
New Mexico	x		x	B_3	
New York	x	C_2			
North Carolina	x	A_1			
North Dakota	xx	A_3			
Ohio	x	A_3			Law is mandatory for crippled children
Oklahoma	x	A_3			No reimbursement provided at present; appropriation bill vetoed
Oregon	x	A_3			
Pennsylvania	x	B_1			
Rhode Island	xx	C_2			
South Carolina			x	D	Appropriation measure for speech correction and hearing program
South Dakota			x	D	
Tennessee	x	A_3			
Texas	x	B_2			
Utah	xx	B_2			Recent appropriations approved to implement law requiring certain programs for physically handicapped
Vermont			xx	C_1	Derived from appropriation bill
Virginia	x	D			
Washington	x	D			
West Virginia			x	D	
Wisconsin	x	B_2			
Wyoming	x	C_1			

SOURCE: Arthur S. Hill, "Extending Special Education through State Legislation," *School Life*, XXXV (1953), 141.
(See next page for Explanation)

Explanation of Table 6

Permissive legislation states that local districts *may* provide special education services.

Mandatory legislation *requires* the establishment of services under certain conditions, i.e., upon petition of parents, the identification of a certain number of handicapped pupils, etc.

The data are compiled from legislative provisions and do not involve local interpretations except in Georgia (see *Remarks*) or modifications due to limited appropriations.

   x Legislation reported by Martens in 1949.

  xx Legislation reported since 1949.

Code for Types of Reimbursement

A. Excess cost formulas:
    A_1 Total excess cost
    A_2 Limited to a stipulated per cent of excess cost
    A_3 Excess cost limited to a stated amount per pupil

B. Prescribed allotments:
    B_1 Per pupil
    B_2 Per class unit, according to a formula
    B_3 For additional teachers

C. Cost of maintaining special classes provided:
    C_1 Total costs
    C_2 Limited to a stipulated per cent of total cost

D. Administrative allotments, no specified formula

school. However, a long-standing condition that is less obvious may be missed by parents but detected by the teacher. The teacher is also in a position to detect early signs of deviation in the nonhandicapped child.

Linck, Shover, and Jacobs give a classification of crippling conditions, as follows:

1. Crippling due to infection (e.g., bone and joint tuberculosis, osteomyelitis, rheumatoid arthritis, syphilis).
2. Cerebral palsy (spacticity, athetosis, ataxia, rigidity, tremors, or variations of these).
3. Crippling due to birth injury (e.g., Erb's palsy, bone fractures).
4. Cardiopathic conditions (e.g., congenital, acquired).
5. Congenital anomalies (e.g., congenital amputation, congenital dislocation, clubfoot, torticollis, spine bifida, cleft lip and palate).
6. Traumatic crippling (e.g., amputation, burns, fractures, joint contracture).
7. Tumors (e.g., bone tumors, bone cysts).
8. Developmental diseases (e.g., coxa plana, spinal osteochondritis).
9. Other conditions (e.g., fragile bones, spinal curvature, postural foot conditions, muscular atrophy, muscular dystrophy, rickets).[2]

The classroom teacher is not expected to have technical familiarity with these conditions, but she should be aware of evident abnormality. Her responsibility is to be on the alert for signs which are indicative of a condition which, if not cared for immediately, may result in a serious development. She should notice, for example:

1. Differences in the level of shoulders or hips.
2. Lack of coordination in muscular activity.
3. Rigidity of muscle groups.
4. Unusual gait or posture.

[2] Lawrence J. Linck, Jayne Shover, and Eveline E. Jacobs, "Teaching the Orthopedically Handicapped and the Cardiopathic," in *The Education of Exceptional Children,* Forty-ninth Yearbook of the National Society for the Study of Education, Part II (Chicago: University of Chicago Press, 1950), pp. 196-97. Quoted by permission of the Society.

Evidence that such appearance or behavior is more than transient is sufficient basis for referral of the child for medical opinion.

Heart

Less conspicuous, because the crippling condition is not obvious, are the victims of heart disorders. The teacher cannot diagnose, but she can be on the lookout for signs such as unexplained labored breathing, chronic fatigue, or a bluish tinge to the lips. These signs may or may not be indications of heart crippling, but they justify referring the child for medical diagnosis. The American Heart Association recommends a therapeutic classification of patients with diseases of the heart as follows:

Class A. Patients with a cardiac disease whose ordinary physical activity need not be restricted.

Class B. Patients with cardiac disease whose ordinary physical activity need not be restricted, but who should be advised against severe or competitive physical efforts.

Class C. Patients with cardiac disease whose ordinary physical activity should be moderately restricted, and whose more strenuous efforts should be discontinued.

Class D. Patients with cardiac disease whose ordinary physical activity should be markedly restricted.

Class E. Patients with cardiac disease who should be at complete rest, confined to bed or chair.[3]

Children diagnosed as having rheumatic fever are a particularly important group in the problem of heart disease, because rheumatic fever is responsible for about 90 per cent of the defective hearts in childhood. Most cases develop between the ages of five and fifteen years, and after the first attack of rheumatic fever, two out of three children are left with heart damage.[4] In some instances the actual signs of

[3] *The Classification of Patients with Diseases of the Heart* (New York: American Heart Association, 1953).

[4] American Heart Association, *Heart Disease in Children* (New York: American Heart Association, 1952), pp. 3, 4.

heart damage, although not evident at first, may develop later in life. In others evidence of damage may disappear. Because one attack of rheumatic fever does not confer immunity to further attacks, exposure to the predisposing condition should be avoided. It has been established that attacks are generally preceded by a streptococcal infection. The statement which follows was issued by the Council on Rheumatic Fever and Congenital Heart Disease of the American Heart Association and summarizes an opinion about the predisposing causes and the general preventive procedures in rheumatic fever:

It is now generally agreed that both the initial and recurrent attacks of the disease are usually precipitated by infections with beta hemolytic streptococci. Therefore, the prevention of rheumatic fever and rheumatic heart disease depends upon the control of streptococcal illnesses. This may be successfully accomplished by early and adequate treatment of streptococcal infections in all individuals and by prevention of streptococcal infections in rheumatic subjects.[5]

The rheumatic child should avoid chilling and must be protected against other individuals who have a cold or sore throat. Medical supervision is necessary during both the active and the inactive stages of rheumatic fever, and close working relationships are required between the physician, home, and school if the best outcome for the child is to be assured.

Children with organic heart disease who are able to take part in ordinary activities (Class A in the classifications above) and those who require varying restriction of physical activity (Classes B and C) may be found in the regular classroom. Those in Classes B and C may tend to tire more quickly than other children, and in some instances, may be poorly adjusted due to improper care at home. The responsibility of the teacher is to follow scrupulously the advice of

---

[5] "The Prevention of Rheumatic Fever," *Public Health Reports*, Publication of the U. S. Public Health Service, LXVIII (1953), 12.

the physician in charge of the pupil. Modification of the pupil's daily program, in the form of a shortened school day and rest periods during the day, may be indicated in some instances. When the case requires substantial modification of school activities, individual guidance is usually needed if the child is to make a good adjustment to his handicap. In larger school systems such pupils are assigned to special classes for cardiac children, or their educational requirements are met by a home teacher provided by the local board of education.

Speech

The largest single group of handicapped children in our schools today is composed of children who have varying degrees of speech defects. More than half of these children have the functional articulatory kind of speech defect in which faulty learning is the common cause. A child omits certain sounds or substitutes one sound for another as is done by an infant learning to talk. A small percentage of the children have organic defects; for example, cleft palate, hearing loss, neuromuscular disorders. About 4 to 6 per cent of the children in school have significant speech disorders and require a specialized correctional program.

The most effective way of finding out which children have speech defects is to have a speech teacher check the pupils or to have the classroom teacher make referrals to the speech teacher. The classroom teacher follows the same general procedure in screening pupils for referral to the speech teacher as she does when she sends pupils to the school nurse. That is, she refers for a special opinion all pupils whose speech is conspicuously (and unaccountably) at variance with that of other members in her group.

When the specialized services of a speech correctionist are not available, the classroom teacher can still be effective in working with children who have speech defects. She continues to be concerned with the remedial and the preventive aspects of the problem. The remedial aspects of the problem require that the teacher work closely with the parents of the child to insure their understanding of the problem and to enlist their cooperation in obtaining medical care when necessary. Source material on procedures for corrective work and other forms of assistance are available through state departments of education. Textbooks on the subject are also available.

In general, the conditions favorable to speech improvement in a given case include (1) sufficient information to make possible on the part of the child, his teachers, and parents a clear understanding of the speech problem and of possible means of dealing with it; (2) encouragement and reward for the speaking done by the child and for the work he does in trying to achieve improvement; (3) elimination of any correctible organic conditions, or compensations for them, such as hearing aids, that place a limit on the possibilities of speech improvement; and (4) social relationships, recreational activities, and personal adjustments conducive to satisfying speech and positive self-evaluations. In some measure these can be provided in most cases by alert teachers and school administrators.[6]

The preventive aspects of speech disorders in general call for a classroom situation which avoids tensions and fears that the child associates with speaking.

Conditions Affecting Speech Adversely Should be Minimized. The conditions in question are mainly those which frustrate speech, or make it an ordeal and a source of disappointment. The undesirable effects of speech disorders are minimized in a highly permissive situation which allows for the relatively free expression of feelings and opinions. The key to the creation of such a situation in the classroom lies largely in maintaining as much informality and "classroom democracy" as are consistent with efficient teaching methods.[7]

[6] Wendell Johnson, "Teaching Children with Speech Handicaps," in *The Education of Exceptional Children*, Forty-ninth Yearbook of the National Society for the Study of Education, Part II (Chicago: University of Chicago Press, 1950), p. 192. Quoted by permission of the Society.

[7] *Ibid.*, p. 191.

Occasionally, the teacher has in her classroom a child handicapped by stuttering. His repetitions, blockages, hesitancies, prolongations, and in some instances, associated physical movements are a source of concern to parent and to teacher alike. The speech of such a child is characterized by fear and by tensions which appear to have their origins in early disapproval of normal hesitancy in speech. Present-day opinion seems to discount an earlier theory that retraining the left-handed child to right-handedness is a causative factor in stuttering.[8] More likely than not, the stuttering began before the child entered school, although it is possible that school experiences contributed to the onset. The best preventive procedures are classroom practices aimed at avoiding experiences which aggravate and may even produce the anxieties and tensions mentioned above.

The child with a speech defect should be encouraged to speak, and the experience should be made a rewarding one for him. If the experience is a rewarding one, which the situation should insure, the objective of correction is more readily achieved.

Epilepsy

Three hundred to four hundred thousand children are estimated to have epilepsy in this country today.[9] The majority of children with epilepsy should be accepted in school, and most of them can be educated in regular classes. Complete medical diagnosis of the child and continuing medical supervision are required. The evidence seems to indicate that epilepsy, as such, is not inherited, but a predisposition to it may be.

We can confirm the opinions which clearminded clinicians have been expressing for many decades. Epilepsy per se is not inherited, but a

[8] Wendell Johnson, et al., "A Study of the Onset and Development of Stuttering," Journal of Speech Disorders, VII (1942), 254.
[9] The Child with Epilepsy, U. S. Children's Bureau Folder No. 35 (Washington, D. C., 1952), p. 6.

"predisposition" or "tendency" may be inherited. A predisposition (heredity) lies dormant until activated by injury or serious disturbance of the brain (environment). Both seed and soil are needed for the growth of epilepsy.[10]

Through advances in medical science, about 50 per cent of children with epilepsy can live under conditions in which attacks are controlled. An additional 30 per cent can have attacks cut down to the point where they are scarcely a handicap. If the epileptic child is given the same educational opportunity as the physically normal child, he has nearly the same potential for learning. His intellectual capacities are not greatly different from those of the nonepileptic child.

There are two types of epilepsy which are more common in childhood. *Petit mal,* almost limited to the young, is the type which is characterized by the child's gazing into space and being unaware of what is going on around him. The attack is usually transient, lasting for only a few seconds, and for this reason, is not always observed by the teacher. *Grand mal,* which occurs at all ages and may be preceded by a warning to the individual, such as dizziness or nausea, is characterized by loss of consciousness and convulsive movements. The child is frequently fatigued at the conclusion of the attack and is in need of rest.

Certain specific instructions should be followed when a pupil has an attack of grand mal in school. All are aimed primarily at preventing the child from hurting himself. The child should be freed from entanglement with chair or desk. It is not necessary to take action merely for the purpose of restraining him during the convulsive state. After he relaxes and regains consciousness, he should be taken from the classroom and allowed to sleep or rest.

Witnessing an attack of grand mal is a disturbing experience to both teacher and pupils alike. It is perhaps unnec-

[10] William G. Lennox, M.D., "Gains Against Epilepsy," *American Medical Association Journal,* CXX (1942), 451.

essary to point out that the attitude of the classroom teacher toward the victim of epilepsy and her behavior at the time of an attack establish the pattern of reaction by pupils in the class.

Epilepsy is a medical problem, and as such, requires the supervision of the family physician or of the school physician. The teacher and the school administrator should be completely informed about the case by the physician and should confer with him concerning the school program for the child. In general, no distinction should be made between the school activities of epileptic and other children. Bradley makes pertinent recommendations, as follows:

It is good practice to tell parents that allowing a child complete participation in whatever activities are available will insure his growing up to the fullest capacity in spite of what other handicaps may remain. By overprotection the actual chance of accident or injury may be slightly reduced, but the net result is a chronic invalid who even if his medical treatment is eventually successful will be left with a feeling of having missed forever a great many desirable childhood experiences. It is to be hoped that the regulations of school systems may progressively be improved as enlightenment on this whole subject becomes dissipated, so that full participation in many activities from which convulsive children are now excluded, especially those of a physical nature, will be encouraged. There is still an unfortunate tendency in many systems to emphasize the possible injury to the child and subsequent complaints or even lawsuits from the family at the expense of what will be most constructive for the child himself and actually reduce the frequency of his seizures.[11]

Quite possibly, certain types of activity bring with them dangers which, for the epileptic child, may be considered disproportionate to the benefits. Handling machinery which is potentially dangerous or swimming in deep water without the presence of adequate safeguards are examples of the kind of activities which medical and educational groups may question for inclusion in the program of the epileptic.

[11] Charles Bradley, "Management of the Convulsive Child," *Rhode Island Medical Journal*, XXIX (1946), 14.

One of the fundamental needs in the problem of epilepsy is adequate understanding by teacher and parents of the emotional and social adjustments required by the epileptic. There may also be substantial need for a sound program of education in the classroom about the responsibility which all share for accepting the epileptic child.

Hearing

At times during her teaching career, every teacher has in her classroom one or more pupils with varying degrees of hearing loss. The classification which follows is suggested as a guide for classifying children with hearing loss:

1. Children with slight losses. These children are on the borderline between normal hearing and significant defective hearing.
2. Children with moderate losses. These are the hard-of-hearing children.
3. Children with marked losses. These children are on the borderline between the hard-of-hearing and the deaf. They do not have enough hearing to learn language and speech with the unaided ear, but they have residual hearing which can be utilized in their education.
4. Children with profound losses. These are the deaf children who do not learn speech and language through their ears even with benefit of amplified sound.[12]

The classroom teacher is ordinarily concerned with children in only the first two categories of the acoustically handicapped; that is, children with slight loss (20 decibels in better ear) and children with moderate loss (25-50 decibels in better ear). Children in the first grouping are those whose hearing is less than normal, but they cannot be classified as

[12] Clarence D. O'Connor and Alice Streng, "Teaching the Acoustically Handicapped," in *The Education of Exceptional Children*, Forty-ninth Yearbook of the National Society for the Study of Education, Part II (Chicago: University of Chicago Press, 1950), p. 153. Quoted by permission of the Society.

deafened. Those in the second grouping do have significant hearing loss for which adjustments should be made in the school program. Generally accepted estimates of the percentage of children of school age with hearing loss range from 4.5 per cent to 6.1 per cent.[13]

Procedures for administering hearing tests to children and interpretation of the findings are discussed in detail in Chapter 4.

The recommended classroom procedure with children who have only slight hearing loss is a periodic recheck to determine whether any change is taking place in hearing acuity. In addition, the pupil is seated in the classroom where his better ear is directed toward the main source of sound.

Children who have an average hearing loss of 25 decibels in the 512 to 2,048 pitch range (speech range) may have need for lip-reading instruction. However, it is advisable to explore every opportunity for remedial medical attention in an attempt to restore hearing before placing dependence on lip-reading skill. The classroom teacher can be instrumental, first, in urging parents to exhaust the possibilities of remedial medical care, and then if lip-reading instruction is necessary, in working closely with the parents and with the lip-reading instructor. The question of whether to recommend hearing aids for children is decided mainly by using the extent of loss as a criterion. Recently, a 35-decibel loss in the better ear was adopted as a minimum for considering the use of a hearing aid. The trend seems to be toward fitting hearing aids to children when there is evidence that the use of an aid will reduce the handicap materially.[14]

Some children among those with moderate hearing loss have need for speech training. This work is included in the

[13] Warren H. Gardner, "Silver Anniversary Report of the Committee on Hard of Hearing Children of the American Society for the Hard of Hearing," Reprint No. 154, *Hearing News* (June and July, 1945), third page.

[14] Lists of approved aids may be obtained from the Council on Physical Therapy, American Medical Association, Chicago.

lip-reading program and is usually the responsibility of a specialist who is employed by the board of education. He works with individuals or small groups several times a week for short periods.

Vision

The visually handicapped may be classified, as follows:

The following types and degree of visual defects are commonly recognized as constituting blindness: (a) central visual acuity of 20/200 or less in the better eye after correction; or (b) visual fields restricted to 20 degrees or less in the widest diameter, without regard to the amount of visual acuity.

Defective vision ranges from slight deviation from normal in any aspect of visual performance to such a severe loss of sight as to constitute blindness as already defined. Within this range a third classification is recognized, namely, "partial sight."[15]

For educational purposes, a partially seeing child is one who has a visual acuity of 20/70 or less in the better eye after the best possible correction, and who can use vision as his chief channel of learning.[16]

The incidence of vision defects in school children is not well established. A report on elementary and high school children of Philadelphia, 1945-46, indicates that 12.7 per cent have visual acuity of 20/30 or poorer.[17] The number of children who are reported to need eye care is substantially greater. In this group are many who are included for reasons other than lowered visual acuity.

The National Society for the Prevention of Blindness estimates 7.5 million school children in the United States are in need of eye care. This estimate is consistent with the finding in the St. Louis study on vision testing methods, cosponsored by the National Society, the Divi-

[15] The National Society for the Prevention of Blindness, Inc., *Eye Health,* Publication No. 447 (New York: National Society for the Prevention of Blindness, Inc., 1946), p. 51.

[16] *Helping the Partially Seeing Child in the Regular Classroom,* Publication No. 156 (New York: National Society for the Prevention of Blindness, Inc., 1953), p. 3.

[17] Metropolitan Life Insurance Company, *Health Bulletin for Teachers,* XXIX, No. 2 (1947), 5.

sion of Public Health of the State of Missouri, the Children's Bureau, and other organizations. In this study the prevalence rate of children with eye conditions requiring observation or treatment by an eye specialist was 27 per cent among first and sixth graders.[18]

The teacher is concerned with (1) children who have simple remediable defects, and (2) those who have somewhat more serious defects. The first group requires follow-up work, the purpose of which is the restoration of functional vision by the use of glasses (see Chap. 4). In addition to diagnosis of the visual defect and the prescription of glasses if necessary, the second group may require modification of the school program for the purpose of conserving vision. This modification takes the form of shortened periods of close visual work alternating with periods of other school activities. The child benefits also from being so placed in the classroom that he has all the advantages of lighting and of proximity to the blackboard.

The present trend seems to be away from the arrangement of special classes for the visually handicapped. Children with more serious visual defects may carry on part of their school work in the regular classroom. Depending on the type and the degree of visual handicap, this constitutes a large or a small part of the school day. During the remainder of the school day, their school work is under the direction of the teacher in charge of a sight conservation class. This arrangement makes possible an educational experience which includes, in general, the same opportunity for the child with partial sight as that enjoyed by the child with normal sight. The handicapped child does not require special privilege, but at the same time, should not experience frustration because of his handicap. He does need modification of his school program to the extent of assuring him op-

---

[18] Arthur J. Lesser, M.D., and Eleanor P. Hunt, Ph.D., "The Nation's Handicapped Children," *American Journal of Public Health*, XLIV (1954), 168.

portunity equal to that of the normal child. The only difference in the curriculum for the visually handicapped is modification of the program at points where medical opinion indicates that the activity (handwork which requires intense visual effort, for example) is not in the best interest of the child.

As with other handicapped children, the classroom teacher and others have responsibility for facilitating the general adjustment of the visually handicapped. For some who have more serious defects, individual attention may be necessary to assist them in making an adjustment to both the regular-class and the special-class groups.

Teeth

Most dental defects are, perhaps, of a less serious nature than many other handicapping conditions. However, the physiological and aesthetic consequences of diseased teeth and of malocclusion should not be dismissed lightly.

Dental defects outrank all other defects of childhood. The most casual inspection of the health record cards of elementary school children or an inspection of the mouths of school pupils by dental hygienist, nurse, or teacher indicates the prevalence of dental defects.

Attempts to reduce dental decay have resulted in emphasis on the cleaning of teeth by brushing. It was hoped that this procedure would reduce the effect on tooth enamel of the acid which is formed in the mouth by the action of lactobacilli on fermentable carbohydrates. However, brushing teeth, as the practice is usually followed, does not insure absence from the mouth of food particles from which lactic acid is formed. If teeth are brushed immediately after eating and the mouth is thoroughly rinsed, there is a possibility that particles of food, including fermentable carbohydrates, will be reduced and that there will be a resulting reduction in the production of lactic acid.

A properly balanced diet in adequate amounts is no longer considered an effective preventive of tooth decay. A direct relationship does exist between caries and the amount of carbohydrate, particularly sugar, in the diet of the child. As excessive amounts of sugar in the diet are cut down, a measure of caries prevention results. Although there is no evidence that an adequate and well-balanced diet reduces the incidence of caries in children, the proper development of teeth and supporting tissues is dependent on the food elements that comprise an adequate diet.

The presence of fluorides in the water supply of a community has been shown to reduce the incidence of caries in the teeth of children. The results of investigations on the use of optimum amounts of fluoride in community water supplies indicate that the reduction in caries may be expected to run as high as 60 per cent in children. A committee, appointed by the Board of Directors of the Commission on Chronic Illness, reviewed the evidence concerning the use of fluorides in community water supplies and reported, in part, as follows:

The basic facts concerning fluoridation which have been established by the investigations of the past 20 years have been briefly set forth in the report of the Ad Hoc Committee on Fluoridation of the National Research Council.[19] Under normal conditions of living, fluorine is a trace element in human nutrition. Although minute amounts are present in certain foods and beverages, a variable and important source is drinking water. Public water supplies vary widely in the amount of fluoride naturally present. Children dependent upon supplies that are low in fluorides have a high dental caries attack rate as compared to children living in communities having water supplies containing about 1 ppm (parts per million) or more of fluoride. The advantage to the latter group is considerable: the incidence of caries is reduced by 1/4 to 2/3. The caries preventive effect of adequate fluoride intake is principally conferred upon children up to the twelfth year of life, during the period when dentine and enamel of permanent dentition

---

[19] "National Research Council Viewpoint on Fluoridation," *Journal American Water Works Association*, XLIV, No. 1 (January, 1952).

are being formed. However, increased resistance to dental caries is carried over into later life to an appreciable degree.

When the trace quantities in drinking water required for optimal dental health are exceeded, undesirable physiological effects may be induced. The most sensitive indication of the latter is interference with normal calcification of the teeth, which is manifested in mottled enamel. This effect, although compatible with caries resistant tooth structure, is esthetically undesirable. The level of fluoride concentration in drinking water which is associated with the appearance of mottled enamel varies with individual susceptibility and the amount of water consumed. Under the climatological conditions of the northern part of the country it is reached when the fluoride content of domestic water supplies exceeds 1.5 ppm.[20]

Arnold, Dean, and Knutson, reporting the carefully controlled Grand Rapids-Muskegon study on the effect of fluoridated public water supplies on the prevalence of dental caries, state, as follows:

A comparison of the 1951 caries rates in Grand Rapids with those of Aurora, Ill., shows that in so far as can be determined to date the use of fluoridated water gives the same beneficial effects as does the use of a natural fluoride water of similar concentration.[21]

Another method which is used to bring fluoride into contact with the teeth of children is referred to as *topical application*. In this procedure the dentist or the dental hygienist applies a solution of sodium fluoride directly to the teeth. It is recommended that children receive treatments when they are about three, seven, ten, and thirteen years of age. Some children do not seem to benefit as much as others from use of fluoridated water or from topical applications. However, the outlook is bright for the vast majority of children who

[20] As quoted in Commission on Chronic Illness, "Effects of Fluoridation of Community Water Supplies upon the Aged and Chronically Ill," *Public Health News*, Publication of the New Jersey State Department of Health (August, 1954), pp. 279-80.
[21] Francis A. Arnold, Jr., D.D.S., H. Trendley Dean, D.D.S., and John W. Knutson, D.D.S., Dr.P.H., "Effect of Fluoridated Public Water Supplies on Dental Caries Prevalence," *Public Health Reports*, Publication of the U. S. Public Health Service, LXVIII (1953), 148.

receive fluoridated water in the optimum concentration—or topical applications of fluoride—during the period when teeth are developing. It is well to point out that the use of fluorides in the prevention of dental caries is only one part of the preventive program in dental health. The need for other dental services still exists.

In addition to dental caries, "a large proportion of all children suffer from malocclusions of varying degrees of severity."[22]   In this condition, the opposing teeth of the jaws do not make proper contact.   The size and the shape of the jaw may cause irregular teeth.   If the dental arch is narrow, crowding and erupting of teeth in other than their normal positions produce a condition in which opposing teeth do not make proper contact.   Severe malocclusions may result from disease or injury to the upper or the lower jaw.   Malocclusion should be observed at the time of the health appraisal.   If a health appraisal which includes oral examination by a dentist or a dental hygienist is not available to pupils, the more obvious malocclusions may be noted by the teacher in her inspection.   Because "periodic dental care of good quality, starting at an early age, does prevent premature tooth loss and overretention of deciduous teeth which may be etiologic factors in malocclusion,"[23] a teacher renders valuable service to the child by calling the attention of the parents to the child's need for dental attention.

SELECTED REFERENCES

AMERICAN HEART ASSOCIATION, COUNCIL ON RHEUMATIC FEVER AND CON-GENITAL HEART DISEASE. "The Prevention of Rheumatic Fever," *Public Health Reports* (Publication of the U. S. Public Health Service), LXVIII (January, 1953), 12-15.

[22] Arthur Bushel, D.D.S., M.P.H., and David B. Ast, D.D.S., M.P.H., "A Rehabilitation Program for the Dentally Physically Handicapped Child," *American Journal of Public Health,* XLIII (1953), 1157.
[23] *Ibid.,* p. 1161.

AMERICAN HEART ASSOCIATION. *Heart Disease in Children.* New York: The Association, 1952.

AMERICAN SPEECH AND HEARING ASSOCIATION, COMMITTEE ON THE MID-CENTURY WHITE HOUSE CONFERENCE. "Speech Disorders and Speech Correction," *Journal Speech and Hearing Disorders,* XVII (June, 1952), 129-37.

ARNOLD, FRANCIS A., JR., D.D.S., DEAN, H. TRENDLEY, D.D.S., and KNUTSON, JOHN W., D.D.S., Dr.P.H. "Effect of Fluoridated Public Water Supplies on Dental Caries Prevalence," *Public Health Reports* (Publication of the U. S. Public Health Service), XLVIII (February, 1953), 141-48.

BALDWIN, RUTH, M.D., DAVENS, EDWARD, M.D., and HARRIS, VIRGINIA, M.D. "The Epilepsy Program in Public Health," *American Journal of Public Health,* XLIII (April, 1953), 452-59.

BUSHEL, ARTHUR, D.D.S., M.P.H., and AST, DAVID B., D.D.S., M.P.H. "A Rehabilitation Program for the Dentally Physically Handicapped Child," *American Journal Public Health,* XLIII (September, 1953), 1156-61.

JOHNSON, WENDELL, *et al. Speech Handicapped School Children.* New York: Harper and Bros., 1948.

LESSER, ARTHUR J., M.D., and HUNT, ELEANOR P., Ph.D. "The Nation's Handicapped Children," *American Journal of Public Health,* XLIV (February, 1954), 166-70.

MACKIE, ROMAINE. *Crippled Children in Schools.* (Publication of the U. S. Office of Education, Bulletin No. 5.) Washington, D. C.: Government Printing Office, 1948.

WALLIN, J. E. W. *Children with Mental and Physical Handicaps.* New York: Prentice-Hall, Inc., 1949.

WILSON, CHARLES C. (ed.). *School Health Services.* Report of the Joint Committee on Health Problems in Education of the National Education Association and the American Medical Association. Washington, D. C.: National Education Association, and Chicago: American Medical Association, 1953, pp. 159-78.

WISHIK, SAMUEL M., and MACKIE, ROMAINE P. "Adjustment of the School Program for the Physically Handicapped Child," *American Journal of Public Health,* XXXIX (August, 1949), 992-98.

Chapter 8

THE PROGRAM OF HEALTH TEACHING

THE understandings, the attitudes, and the habits of the school child in matters of health are acquired from many sources of experience which make up his daily living.

Responsibilities in Health Teaching

If we accept that the home is the first bulwark in our program for child health, fundamental responsibility for the habits of a child which affect his health rests with the home. As a matter of fact, the classroom teacher becomes keenly aware, in many instances, of the influence of the home in matters of health behavior when she attempts to change the child's behavior to conform with suggested hygienic practices or with recommendations of health specialists. Resistance, prejudice, misconception are all met by the teacher in her contacts with the homes of children. For example, the instructional program which includes information about nutrition and reference to the kinds of food which comprise an adequate diet has little chance of becoming effective if the instruction runs counter to firmly established dietary practices in the home. The thoughtful teacher or health specialist realizes that the home from which the child comes sometimes needs guidance in health matters before improvement in child understandings and behavior can be brought about.

In addition to the home, community influences on the child are instrumental in the formation of health concepts and practices. For example, whether the work is well done or poorly done, community waste disposal is a constant reminder to the child of the way in which his community meets this problem. His feelings about this particular aspect of community health and his concept of standards in reference to it are determined by his observation of the way in which the work is done. Because he knows no others, these standards become desirable standards for him. Other activities in community sanitation, which are carried on by the public health authorities and which the child observes, exert a similar influence in establishing his standards for the activities.

The general organization of the school health program provides, among other things, for—

1. General health services, which call for the attention of specialists in the field of health, as physicians, dentists, nurses. In the work of health appraisal and follow-up for the correction of remediable defects, the primary purpose of school health department specialists is educational. These services are concerned with preventing conditions that are inimical to the child's development, with referring him for correction of remediable defects and with modifying conditions which interfere with his health welfare. For example, he takes screening tests and is referred for clinical attention, if necessary, as part of the preventive program in tuberculosis; he may be referred for opinion about the removal of tonsils and adenoids. The clinical services to which the child is referred for diagnosis are supplied by private practitioners on a private physician-patient basis, or they may be provided by the official health or welfare agency or by a voluntary health agency in the community. The board of education does not provide remedial clinical work.

2. Health instruction designed to insure appropriate health behavior through the development of desirable attitudes, habits, and understandings.

Bases for Program Development

The instructional program, designed to promote appropriate health behavior, utilizes recognized procedures, such as problem solving and large units of work, to achieve desired outcomes. Regardless of the procedures used in the health instruction program, need exists for definite planning on the part of the teacher to insure (1) the desired outcomes in terms of attitudes, habits, and understandings; (2) a suitable content for the program; (3) an appropriate methodology for the program; and (4) techniques for evaluating the program.

The development of appropriate attitudes toward desirable health behavior are always stressed in the field of health education. This suggests we may well inquire briefly into the process by means of which such attitudes are developed. Allport's definition of an attitude has been widely quoted:

> *An attitude is a mental and neural state of readiness, organized through experience, exerting a directive or dynamic influence upon the individual's response to all objects and situations with which it is related.*[1]

The same author describes four ways in which attitudes are formed:

One of the chief ways in which attitudes are built up is through the accretion of experience, that is to say, through the *integration* of numerous specific responses of a similar type. It is not, as a rule, the discrete and isolated experience which engenders an attitude; for in itself the single experience lacks organization in memory, meaning, and emotion. An attitude is characteristically a fusion, or, in Burn-

[1] Gordon W. Allport, "Attitudes," in *A Handbook of Social Psychology*, ed. Carl Murchison (Worcester, Mass.: Clark University Press, 1935), p. 810.

ham's terms . . . , a "residuum of many repeated processes of sensation, perception and feeling.". . .

. . . the original matrix of all attitudes is coarse, diffuse, and nonspecific; it is the mass-action found in infancy, which tends only to have a general positive (adient) or negative (abient) orientation. From this point of view, it might be said that in the beginning the infant has two primordial, nonspecific attitudes, namely, approaching and avoiding. From this matrix, he must segregate action-patterns and conceptual systems which will supply him with adequate attitudes for the direction of his adaptive conduct. . . .

It is well known that a permanent attitude may be formed as the result of a compulsive organization in the mental field following a single intense emotional experience. Probably everyone can trace certain of his fears, dislikes, prejudices, and predilections to dramatic incidents of childhood. . . . there is all through life a susceptibility to the influence of emotional shock. . . . Even in old age radical changes of attitude through circumstances of dramatic moment are not unknown. . . .

Through the imitation of parents, teachers, or playmates, they (attitudes) are sometimes adopted *ready-made.*[2]

A report, *Emotion and the Educative Process,* about the role of education in the genesis of attitude reads:

The importance of the experiences of childhood and adolescence for the establishment of attitudes has been stressed. The school has its genuine place as the locus of many of these experiences; but its purposed influence in many cases is not the determining factor in the attitudes which emerge. The family, playmates, and schoolmates, accidents and events of wider social consequences (disasters, political campaigns, strikes, economic depressions, wars) all are influential in the situations where concept crystallization takes place and attitudes are born. None the less, the role of the school remains highly important.

In the first place, it is the task of the school to expose the individual to a great body of facts. These facts need to be sufficiently balanced and broad to lessen the likelihood that attitudes will be founded on biased or inadequate knowledge.

In the second place, it is the school which must help children to understand the dynamic nature of life and of social processes. As children understand the present as a point along the path of the

2 *Ibid.,* pp. 810-11.

physical, social, and spiritual evolution of mankind, they may come to understand and expect the necessity for further adjustments and changes which will involve themselves and their own attitudes.[3]

Although expressed for general education, this point of view is no less significant when applied to the problem of developing attitudes in the field of health education. Rapid advances in techniques of early diagnosis and, more particularly, in specific therapy of human ills suggest the need for constantly changing attitudes. For example, the position formerly taken by many educators toward school attendance by an epileptic child is now untenable, in most instances, in view of a better comprehension of the problem and the development of more effective means for the control of epilepsy.

The primary purpose of health teaching in the lower grades is rather commonly stated to be the development of health habits. Although it may appear easy to accomplish this purpose, care should be taken not to assume that desirable habits are being established by the children when the teacher directs and controls all situations. The child must have information and concepts about health behavior, appropriate to his level of understanding, if he is to develop desirable health habits. In the upper grades the pupil has need for a basic body of knowledge which will enable him to make desirable choices in health behavior. Without such a body of knowledge he has only the directive force of habit or of attitudes founded on inadequate knowledge as a basis for directing his own health behavior. Such limited resources lack the flexibility required for meeting new or unusual situations. This need for flexibility is well stated in *Health Education:*

In the more or less unpredictable current of events that characterize daily living a certain amount of judgment must always be exercised.

[3] Committee on the Relation of Emotion to the Educative Process, ch. Daniel A. Prescott (Washington, D. C.: American Council on Education, 1938), pp. 87-88.

The exercise of judgment is possible only when the individual has adequate factual knowledge and a certain insight and power of analysis which enable him to determine whether any of his readymade responses suffice in his immediate, real-life circumstances or whether he perhaps needs to develop new responses.[4]

Programs of instruction which associate the child and his interests with his personal health needs and with community, home, and school health needs bring to him an ever-widening understanding of health problems and his relationship to them. The teacher and the pupils plan the kind of educational experiences which, at different grade levels help to develop this understanding.

There is no generally accepted procedure in health instruction for the elementary grades. In many schools it is common practice to stress incidental teaching in which advantage is taken of an episode in school or community life to emphasize pertinent health understandings and practices. Such a procedure may or may not be accompanied by a specific allotment of time for health instruction. Incidental teaching is commonly used in the lower grades. In the upper elementary grades a specific time allotment is made for instruction in health in the belief that such an allotment will insure attention to health teaching.

Determination of Content of Program

In general, the content of the health teaching program is determined by the needs and interests of the child.

Needs of Child

Various sources provide information that is useful in determining these needs, which may be grouped under headings as follows:

[4] National Education Association and American Medical Association, Joint Committee on Health Problems in Education, ed. Charles C. Wilson (4th ed.; Washington, D. C.: National Education Association, 1948), p. 182.

1. Freedom from accidents
2. Freedom from preventable illness and death
3. Opportunity for optimum growth and development
4. Desirable attitudes and practices in mental, emotional, and physical health

Certain health needs of children which provide the purpose and the basis for content in the instructional program can be determined by an inspection of mortality and morbidity reports on large and representative groups of children. These reports indicate the child health problems that actually exist in the United States. A study of them should provide a basis, in part, for determining the content of the health teaching program.

Mortality figures show the leading causes of death for the five to fourteen years age group (see Table 7). The first item indicates the need for safety education in the school health program. Other items in the list suggest other specific needs in the program, although these items do not lend themselves as readily to instruction in the classroom.

TABLE 7

DEATHS AND DEATH RATES FOR FIVE LEADING CAUSES OF DEATH IN 5–14 YEARS AGE GROUP, UNITED STATES, 1950

Rank Order		Rate per 100,000
	All Races, Both Sexes	60.1
1	Accidents	22.7
	Motor vehicle accidents	8.8
	All other accidents	13.8
2	Malignant neoplasms, including neoplasms of lymphatic and hematopoietic tissues	6.7
3	Influenza and pneumonia, except pneumonia of newborn	3.2
4	Acute poliomyelitis	2.5
5	Congenital malformations	2.4
	All other causes	22.6

SOURCE: U. S. Public Health Service, National Office of Vital Statistics, "Leading Causes of Death," *Vital Statistics-Special Reports*, XXXVII (December 16, 1953), Table 2, p. 387.

From her own state department of health, the teacher may obtain mortality and morbidity figures which indicate the presence of specific health problems peculiar to her own locality. In certain geographic areas of the United States some problems are more prevalent than in other areas. For example, in certain parts of the country the incidence of rheumatic fever and resulting rheumatic heart disease is higher than in others. In this case, emphasis in the instructional program is suggested on the avoidance, as far as this is possible, of repeated respiratory infection. Although we do not have specific means for preventing respiratory infection, children should be urged to change from wet footgear when necessary, to wear clothing which is suitable for the season, and to avoid chilling of the body. Hookworm is more of a problem in the southern part of the United States than it is in the northern part. The *relative* need for emphasis on reparative work on teeth may be reduced in certain sections where the amount of fluorine in the water supply reduces the incidence of decay in children's teeth.

Local health reports when published weekly or biweekly can be useful in determining the content of the health instruction program of the school. These reports make available to the teacher information about the incidence of childhood communicable disease. She can utilize this information in her incidental teaching program. Reports of the official health department indicate the number and the kinds of cases of illness that are reported by practicing physicians to the department. Some of the more common childhood communicable diseases are not always reported, but scarlet fever and measles usually are. The extent to which information of this kind is of value in determining the content of the health teaching program is problematical. As was mentioned in Chapter 5, some child health specialists hold the opinion that an inexpensive way of obtaining immunity to certain childhood communicable diseases is for the child to have an attack of these diseases during early years. If this point of view is held by the department responsible for the control of communicable disease in school, the classroom teacher is less concerned with the usual procedures which are aimed at controlling childhood communicable disease. However, unless the school health department is definitely operating under the newer plan for childhood communicable disease control, the procedures of the older and more firmly established method should govern when the teacher determines the content of the instructional program about childhood communicable disease.

The cumulative health records of children furnish evidence of the presence of health problems which involve the more common structural and functional defects of childhood. Some of these defects are irremediable. Among these are certain kinds of heart defects. In these cases, the school's main contribution to the child's welfare is a modified school program, and if necessary, individual help in his problems of adjustment. Therefore, evidence of the presence of health problems which involve irremediable defects offers little to the classroom teacher when she is planning the content of her health instruction program. However, there are other defects which can be prevented or corrected. Among these are dental defects and poor nutritional status. As items on the cumulative record card, these defects rank high in the total number of *positive findings* (indications of conditions other than normal) at the time of the health appraisal. This suggests that when determining the content of the instructional program the teacher should give substantial attention to the whole problem of remediable defects, their prevention, and their correction.

As reports of board of education departments of pupil accounting show, the majority of absences from school are caused by illness. The teacher is aware of this as a result of keeping her register, on which the greatest single, stated cause of absence is invariably illness. An inspection of a list of the specific illnesses causing absence from school is informative. A report by the Metropolitan Life Insurance Company of a study made in seven selected cities in California shows the greatest percentage of absence is due to respiratory infection (see Fig. 12). The implication for em-

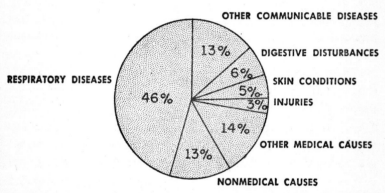

FIGURE 12. What Are the Causes for Children's Absences? Source: *Absent from School Today* (New York: Metropolitan Life Insurance Company, 1949), p. 5. Courtesy of the Metropolitan Life Insurance Company.

phasis in the teaching program is clear. Possibly, very little respiratory illness in children can be avoided with the present limited preventive techniques available to the classroom teacher. However, an emphasis on the accepted preventive procedures, such as avoiding contacts with infected individuals, hand-washing, and taking precautions against chilling the body, may well be included in the content of the instructional program.

The health needs of children for normal growth and development provide a purpose and a further basis for content of the instructional program. A determination of needs of this kind is made by the physician as part of his appraisal

of the child. The needs may be concerned with the kinds
and the amount of food necessary or with an adequate program of sleep and rest, for example. In this is a suggestion
that certain aspects of the health services program can be
easily and profitably associated with the program of health
instruction.

The child also has need for the kind of health behavior
that meets accepted standards. This behavior may be acquired as a result of an instructional program (1) in which
the primary objective is good habit formation, as in the lower
grades; or (2) in which, as a result of an understanding of
good hygienic practices, the objective is the ability to make
intelligent choices in health behavior, as in the upper grades.
For example, the teacher inquires and learns about the eating
habits of the children in her classroom and relates this information to the instructional program in nutrition; she may
urge children to eat their lunches in an unhurried fashion
and to choose an appropriate lunch pattern from the seven
basic foods. The school lunch program, which is sponsored
by the educational authorities and is operated by the schools
in the majority of cases, offers an unusual opportunity for
instruction in nutrition. The program is a continuing one
and may be used by the teacher in applying many of her
classroom teachings in health.

As a basis for determining the content of the instructional
program or as a basis for carrying on her health guidance, a
classroom teacher in a particular school or community may
wish to conduct an investigation of the health needs of the
children in her class. The procedures which follow are
recommended for such a project:

Study of the health needs of children attending a particular school
will provide data that are helpful in evaluating what has been accomplished in the past and in planning what needs to be done in the
future. Procedures useful in securing such data are:

1. Compilation of figures on the per cent of children who have been immunized against such preventable diseases as smallpox, diphtheria, whooping cough, and tetanus. Children should receive treatment to prevent these diseases long before they enter school, preferably during the first year of life.

2. Analysis of causes of sickness. This is likely to show that colds and sore throat are important symptoms of sickness, and leading causes of absence from school. At certain ages the communicable diseases of childhood cause considerable sickness.

3. Analysis of causes of death of school age children. Mortality statistics reveal that in most parts of the country accidents, rheumatic heart disease, and pneumonia are the chief causes of death.

4. Compilation of teachers' observations of the appearance and behavior of pupils. This provides valuable information concerning both the physical and mental health of pupils.

5. Compilation of the results of medical examinations of pupils. If pupils have not had medical examinations, plans should be made for this service.

6. Survey of pupils' diets. Does each pupil have the basic seven foods daily?

7. Survey of the number of pupils whose teeth were treated or examined by a dentist during the preceding six months. Did they have sodium fluoride applications to reduce dental decay?[5]

In addition to the health needs of children, as determined by the procedures mentioned above, are needs specifically associated with the child's behavior. Everyday school experiences shed some light on the health habits of children, but a joint home-school survey is much more satisfactory. Information about eating habits, rest and sleep, and practices of personal cleanliness, for example, may be obtained through cooperation with the home. A questionnaire on health habits, used by the Tuttle Demonstration School of the

[5] Charles C. Wilson, "Planning Together for Good Health," in *Health in the Elementary School*, Twenty-ninth Yearbook of the Department of Elementary School Principals, National Education Association (Washington, D. C.: National Education Association, 1950), p. 13.

QUESTIONNAIRE ON HEALTH HABITS
(Tuttle Demonstration School, University of Minnesota)

NAME_____ROOM_____DATE_____

TO PARENTS:

Many of the health problems of children have to do with establishing a plan for daily living which meets the individual's health needs. In order that we may help your child to understand and plan for his own needs, it is necessary that we have some knowledge of his daily habits. May we ask that you help your child to complete accurately the following form, giving us this important information?

Food Habits

1. Which of the following groups of foods do you eat? [Code for replies: (1) Daily, (2) Occasionally, (3) Not at all]
   A. Milk _____
   B. Vegetables_____
   C. Fruit _____
   D. Meat, Cheese, Fish_____
   E. Eggs _____
   F. Cereal or bread_____
   G. Butter _____
2. Do you eat your meals at regular times?_____
3. Do you eat between meals? Frequently _____ Occasionally _____ Seldom _____
4. At what time and what foods do you eat between meals?_____
5. Do your bowels move regularly without help?_____
6. Do you have any trouble with frequent urination?_____

Rest

7. At what time do you usually go to bed at night? _____
8. At what time do you usually get up in the morning?_____
9. Do you sleep alone?_____
10. Is your sleep disturbed in any way? _____ If so, how?_____
11. Do you have any rest periods during the day?_____ If so, when and for how long?_____

Cleanliness

12. Do you wash your hands after going to the toilet?_____ Before eating?_____
13. Do you have a sponge or tub bath daily?_____
14. How often do you put on clean clothing?_____
15. How often do you brush your teeth?_____

Out of School Activities

16. What do you usually do after school?_____
17. What do you usually do on Saturdays and Sundays?_____
18. What regular duties do you have outside of school?_____

Medical Care

19. Do you have regular examinations by your own physician?
20. When were you last examined by your own physician?_____
21. What are your personal health needs?_____
22. How often do you have your teeth examined by your dentist?
23. Questions and comments of parent and child_____

University of Minnesota, indicates the kind of information which is obtained by a home-school survey (see Fig. 13).

Interests of Child

In addition to the health needs of children as determined by the official records of health problems and by the opinion of adults, the interests of the child himself point to needs which for him are important. When young children are carefully studied, many of their activities seem meaningless to adults, but these activities are interesting to children and educative. Gwynn[6] finds children are interested in—

Activities which satisfy the creative urge
Care of the body and the prevention of disease
Care of pets and animals
Exploration of their own environment
Growth of plants, animals, and human beings
Machines which serve mankind
Museums
Newsstands and newsstand literature
Other people and races
Pictures
Radio, television, moving pictures
Recreation and play of all types

Some of these general interests of children have a relationship to health and might determine, in part at least, some of the characteristics of the instructional program.

The teacher realizes that inventories used to discover a child's interests may be unduly colored by a singular occur-

[6] J. Minor Gwynn, *Curriculum Principles and Social Trends* (New York: The Macmillan Co., 1950), pp. 279-84.

FIGURE 13. Questionnaire on Health Habits. Source: Ella Christensen, Florence Pederson, and W. W. Staudenmaier, "Coordinating Services and Instruction," in *Health in the Elementary School,* Twenty-ninth Yearbook of the Department of Elementary School Principals, National Education Association (Washington, D. C.: National Education Association, 1950), p. 142.

rence, such as a recent epidemic of childhood disease and particularly an epidemic which is accompanied by fatal outcomes. Nevertheless, the child's interest is genuine at the time, although it is influenced by a dramatic and comparatively unusual event.

A report of a survey[7] from the elementary schools of Herlong, California, indicates by grade level which of twenty "areas of health" were of most interest to children at the time of the survey. The children's interest in the areas was indicated in replies to 264 questions.

Grade 4. Physical development, growth, and care of eyes

Grade 5. Protection from disease, elementary physiology, first-aid and care of sick

Grade 6. Protection from atomic attack, communicable disease control (poliomyelitis), control of emotion (temper)

Grade 7. Communicable disease control (poliomyelitis), exercise, orthopedics (flat feet)

Grade 8. Personal appearance (skin condition), personality development (mixed group activities), communicable disease control (poliomyelitis)

Of equal importance in determining program content are the items of least interest to pupils. Smith reports certain areas of health in that classification, as follows:

Grade 4. School health, heredity, eugenics, and selection of foods

Grade 5. School health, safety, and good eating habits

Grade 6. Good eating habits, home nursing and health, and dental health

Grade 7. Good eating habits, home nursing and health, and school health

Grade 8. Safety, dental health, and school health[8]

[7] H. Lawson Smith, "Ask the Children," in *Health in the Elementary School*, Twenty-ninth Yearbook of the Department of Elementary School Principals, National Education Association (Washington, D. C.: National Education Association, 1950), pp. 195-97.

[8] *Ibid.*, p. 197.

Although these areas are reported as being of little interest to pupils, many of them are of substantial concern to the health specialist and the classroom teacher in determining content for health instruction. If, after surveying her own pupils, a classroom teacher finds a similar lack of pupil interest in certain areas of health, the implication is clear. If her findings show items of interest and items of least interest as in Grade 4 in the report above, she brings out through pupil experiences the relationship between the *selection of foods,* in which pupils are little interested, and *physical development,* in which pupils are markedly interested.

Principles Governing Choice of Experiences

Classroom practices in health teaching are influenced, to some extent, by the manner in which the curriculum of the school is organized. The teacher in the lower elementary grades commonly uses broad topics of general interest to pupils, and in addition, utilizes incidental opportunities which have value because they are timely. General interest in first aid and care of the sick, for example, can quite easily be associated with the care of simple accidents or sudden illness occurring in the classroom or on the school grounds. In some schools the upper elementary grades may be organized on the basis of a specific time allotment for various subjects. In others segmentation of the curriculum is avoided by utilizing units of work which provide broad learning experiences for the pupil.

If the teacher conducts her classroom teaching program with the conviction that the learning which takes place has a quality related to the pupil's experiences, she regards her part in the choice and direction of experiences as particularly significant. Certain well-established principles should guide her in developing classroom experiences that achieve the purposes of the program. She may use the statement of principles which follows, as a guide in instructional processes:

1. Teachers should, as a first step in instruction, have clearly formulated in their minds the educational objectives they are to attain through the instructional process. This means that if a teacher undertakes to develop a unit of study . . . , he should know what the children ought to derive from the experience.

2. Educational objectives should be translated into behavior patterns—patterns of knowing, understanding, appreciating, desiring, adjusting, doing, and thinking that become functional aspects of the child's daily living.

3. Educational objectives become patterns of response of the type just enumerated as children have the guided experiences designed to achieve these objectives.

4. The primary task of the teacher is to manipulate the classroom environment so that children will have educative experiences. This manipulation takes the form of selecting and organizing experiences which are educative and of guiding and directing children in these experiences.

5. New behavior patterns, both desirable and undesirable, are established in terms of the goals which children themselves attempt to reach through their activity.

6. Goals for learning activity are established in terms of children's motives—their wants, needs, interests, or drives.

7. A first step in the actual instructional process is to formulate, with the children as participants, the goals to be attained as they work and learn.

8. Content and activity are means to ends, these ends being new behavior patterns. Content and activity are not ends in themselves.

9. Learning takes place or fails to take place in terms of the individual child. While instruction is usually a group procedure, learning is always an individual process.

10. The teacher as an individual personality is an important element in the learning environment. The way in which his personality interacts with the personalities of the children being taught helps to determine the kind of behavior which emerges from the learning situation.

11. Interpersonal interactions . . . are important elements in the learning environment. These personal interactions are in part responsible for the kinds of social, emotional, and intellectual behavior which emerge in the learning situation.

12. Evaluation is an integral part of the instructional process. Teachers and pupils should be continuously considering together the contribution of different experiences to goals sought. The on-going experiences should be reconstructed in light of the evaluations being made.[9]

Plan for Purposeful Program

With these principles as a basis, the teacher needs next a logical plan for making her instructional program purposeful. From the steps in the scientific method as applied in education by Good, Barr, and Scates,[10] Grissom has adapted a series of steps for logical planning for health instruction:

Steps in Planning

Step A: *A definition of the problem.* In health teaching this means that we must find the unmet health education needs of our pupils. For example, our pupils are able, and are usually expected, to know, understand, act, and refrain from acting in certain ways for achieving and maintaining optimum health. We must determine which part of this knowledge, these understandings, skills for actions, habits, and attitudes our pupils should, but do not now possess. The *problem* then is to provide the necessary experiences for gaining knowledge, understandings, habits, attitudes, and skills for action that our pupils do not already possess. We can say that *Step A is to discover the unmet health education needs of our pupils.*

Step B: *Survey available data.* In health teaching this means to consider the nature of and capabilities of our pupils. It means to consider sound educational procedures. It means to consider the best resources and materials available, space needed, facilities, and even our own capabilities and limitations. In other words it means to bring into use all known sound educational theory that is applicable to the problem in our situ-

[9] G. Lester Anderson, Gertrude Whipple, and Robert Gilchrist, "The School as a Learning Laboratory," in *Learning and Instruction,* Forty-ninth Yearbook of the National Society for the Study of Education, Part I (Chicago: University of Chicago Press, 1950), pp. 337-38.

[10] C. V. Good, A. S. Barr, and D. E. Scates, *The Methodology of Educational Research* (New York: D. Appleton-Century Co., 1935), pp. 16-24.

ation.   We can say that *Step B* is *to survey all available resources.*

Step C: *Formulate an hypothesis.* In health teaching this means to make the most logical plan possible which would seem to give our pupils an opportunity to acquire the needed knowledge, understandings, skills for action, habits, and attitudes for optimum health.   Usually a planned program for teaching health includes such things as:

1. A definite pupil objective
2. A definite list of pupil activities aimed at accomplishing the objective
3. A definite list of needed materials and resources for carrying out the activities
4. A definite list of ways to collect evidence about what the students accomplished toward achieving the objectives.

We can say that *Step C* is *to plan an educational program.*

Step D: *Test the hypothesis.* In health teaching this means to put our educational plans described in *Step C* into operation, using the planned activities, materials and resources. We can say that *Step D* is *to put our plans into action.*

Step E: *Collect the new data.* In health teaching this means to bring together all evidences of pupil achievements in acquiring knowledge, understandings, skills for actions, habits, and attitudes. We can say that *Step E* is *to collect all evidences of growth in learning.*

Step F: *Analyze, classify, and summarize the new data.* In health teaching this means to classify our evidences as nearly as possible into some meaningful order such as *habits acquired, knowledge gained, skills learned, false beliefs and practices discarded,* and so on. We can say that *Step F* is *to analyze the results of our teaching.*

Step G: *Make generalizations.* In health teaching this means to conclude, in light of the evidences collected, that the planned program was successful, only partly successful, or a complete failure. We can say that *Step G* is *to make an evaluative statement regarding the results of our program.*[11]

[11] Deward K. Grissom, "A Health Teaching Guide for Tennessee Teachers, Its Background and Production" (Doctor's thesis, Advanced School of Education, Teachers College, Columbia University, 1952), pp. 27-29.

As mentioned in the steps involved in applying the scientific method to health teaching, a planned program includes, among other things, such items as pupil objectives, activities, resources and materials, and evaluation techniques. Many textbooks have been primarily written about health instruction, and many courses of study in health have been prepared by state departments of education. In these texts and courses of study the teacher will find examples of planned programs which include the items mentioned above. An example of how certain health objectives for Grades 4, 5, and 6 may be realized through planned experiences is found in the *Tennessee Course of Study in Health Education for Grades 1 Through 12* (see Table 8).

Interrelationships for Health Instruction

In the development of experiences, in the utilization of incidental opportunities for learning, and in the arrangement of large teaching units the health services program of the school should receive considerable emphasis. The health examination, the dental inspection, and the inspection by the school nurse are examples of routine practices which, when associated by the teacher with her classroom health teaching program, can have substantial significance for the pupil. The pupil gains an understanding of the purposes of such procedures, and the part he plays in them is quite different from the passive role he assumes when understanding of them is lacking.

Opportunities for interrelationships are also present between health instruction, on the one hand, and social studies, general science, the school lunch, and physical education, on the other. Classroom activities that are planned to demonstrate the responsibilities of the individual to the community in which he lives and the responsibilities of local government to the individual, the application of elementary learnings in

TABLE 8

If our pupil needs call for objectives such as these	*Here are some suggested pupil activities*
1. To acquire beginning knowledge that proper growth depends upon a wise selection of foods.	1. a) Keep a record of food eaten for three days. b) Keep a record of own weight and height. c) Plant corn, wheat, and other seed in a box in the classroom and observe growth. d) Take field trips in the spring to observe the growth of leaves and plants. e) Assume responsibility for feeding pets.
2. To develop a liking for a wider variety of foods and an increased willingness to try new foods.	2. a) Plan and take trip to a market or garden to see food growing or to purchase food. b) Make charts or arrange models showing suitable food for breakfast and other meals. c) Make and use food models showing selection of basic seven food groups for different meals. d) Cooperate with lunchroom manager in planning school luncheon. e) Use colored cards placed on individual lunch trays for evaluation of lunches as: excellent, fair, or poor.
3. To develop an understanding that it is better to drink milk or eat fruit between meals than it is to eat sweets.	3. a) Make an occasional survey of own class, comparing money spent for fruits and candy during one entire week. b) Collect facts comparing nutritional value of milk, fruit, sweets. c) Entertain other groups and serve foods good for in-between snacks. d) View and discuss films.

TABLE 8 (*continued*)

Here are some suggested resources and materials	*Here are some suggested evaluation helps*

1. a) Own class members.
  b) Height and weight cards.
  c) Seeds and containers from home.
  d) Local field.
  e) Own pets at home.
	1. Do the children eat breakfast, lunch, and dinner (supper)?
	Has an interest in learning more about foods been shown?
	Do the children show improvement in selecting and eating foods from each of the basic seven groups?
	Are there visible signs of health as shown by:
	Sparkling eyes?
	Glossy hair?
	Happy, cheerful attitude?
	Adequate gain in height and weight?

2. a) Local garden, or local food market.
  b) Carefully selected pictures of foods from magazines.
  c) Material for making food models. Casein glue (powdered) and paper towels. (These towels can be soaked in the glue, wrapped around real food, dried, and painted).
  d) Foods being served in cafeteria.
  e) Colored cards and student observer from own class to place cards on trays of class members at end of selection line.
	2. Are the children selecting a wider variety of desirable foods?
	Do the children enjoy trying out new foods?
	Do the children like to evaluate their lunch trays?

3. a) Own class members.
  b) Textbooks, reference books, library books.
  c) Apples, oranges, dried fruits, fruit juices, raw green and yellow vegetables.
  d) Film such as: "Fun in Food."
	3. Are the children drinking milk rather than carbonated drinks?
	Are the pupils eating fruits when served?
	Do the pupils participate freely in the discussion?
	Are the pupils making wise selections in spending money for snacks?

TABLE 8 (*continued*)

If our pupil needs call for objectives such as these	*Here are some suggested pupil activities*
4. To gain knowledge of why food should not be wasted.	4. a) Have a committee to check on wasted food in the lunchroom by daily inspection of garbage pail. b) Discuss why this food is wasted and ways of eliminating it. c) Take a trip to the grocery store and list cost of foods to estimate the cost of the food wasted in the lunchroom. d) Invite a resource person who has had personal contact with other countries to talk to class on need for better food for children in other lands.
5. To develop an appreciation for pleasant family association during meal time. NOTE TO TEACHER: Caution will have to be practiced here in order to avoid embarrassing some members of the class when discussing home situations. Concentrate on school lunches as much as possible.	5. a) Survey our class members to see what meals the whole family eat together in the home. b) Tell the class about holiday and festive dinners served in our home. Discuss why everyone has fun at these dinners. c) Study and practice good table manners in the classroom and in the school cafeteria.
6. To learn that diseases can be spread through unsanitary foods.	6. a) Select some foods from the lunchroom and put in jars. Put some pure water in some jars. Place some jars in the refrigerator and others in the sun or in a warm place. Smell the foods and water in the refrigerated jars the next day and compare with those put in a warm place. b) Examine under a microscope a drop of fluid from the refrigerated jars and the nonrefrigerated jars. c) Read and discuss why the bacteria grew in the warm jars.

TABLE 8 (*continued*)

Here are some suggested resources and materials	Here are some suggested evaluation helps
4. a) Class members and own school cafeteria. b) Lunchroom manager. c) Local grocery store. d) Someone from local community such as exchange teacher, displaced person, foreign students, returned soldier, or travelers.	4. Did the amount of food waste in lunchroom garbage decrease as the study progressed? Do the actions and comments of the pupils show that they are anxious to conserve food? Were there evidences, such as questions, comments, and actions, that the pupils had become concerned over their waste of food?
5. a) Class members. b) Class members. c) Text and other books and pamphlets on good table manners. Silverware from cafeteria for demonstrations.	5. Do the pupils enjoy eating their lunch? Do the pupils use good table manners during meals at school? Do the pupils enjoy telling of holiday festivals? Do the mothers of the pupils show an interest in the good manners program?
6. a) Refrigerator jars, refrigerator, and samples of foods from the cafeteria. b) Samples treated as in "a". c) Microscope from the science laboratory. d) Text, books, pamphlets, and other materials from library.	6. Are the children continuing to wash hands before eating? Are the children aware that bacteria grow quickly in foods and not in pure water? Are the children beginning to understand what bacteria are?

SOURCE: Tennessee Department of Education and Tennessee Department of Public Health, *Tennessee Course of Study in Health Education for Grades 1 Through 12* (Nashville: Tennessee Department of Education and Tennessee Department of Public Health, 1952), pp. 48-9.

science to home and community sanitation, and the relationship of good nutrition to the choice of foods can all have significance for the pupil when he is able to relate classroom activities to occurrences in his daily life and to his personal interests. Practices connected with sleep and rest and with heating and ventilation in the home may be associated with classroom instruction. Community practices concerned with the food supply and the water supply and with the control of childhood communicable disease may be related at the level of the pupil's understanding to large units of experience, such as "How Our Food Supply Is Protected" or "Life in Our Community."

Development of Understandings

The techniques of teaching used by the teacher should aid in motivating the pupil to further activity and should produce critical thinking and understanding appropriate to his grade level. The effective program in health teaching associates the school health teaching program with real problems in health. Some are problems of personal health and are associated with the needs of the individual; others are problems of public health and are associated with the individual's understanding of community health needs. The effective program places substantial weight on outcomes in terms of understandings and behavior. The intelligent basis for choice in health matters rests on understandings in personal and community health. Brownell and Sims call attention to a number of elements in the teaching-learning situation which they indicate must be present if understanding is to be expected:

a) Understanding depends largely on the degree to which the pupil is motivated initially by a recognized need. The relation of understanding to need . . . is exactly the point at which teachers so often fail. Whether or not any worth-while learning results from activity which is not purposeful to the child, that is, from activity which he does not recognize as meeting needs which he considers important, we will not dwell upon. Certain it is that only limited understanding comes from such activity. The emphasis on "doing something" found in many so-called activity schools does not necessarily result in learning that is more meaningful than that which occurs in the most highly formalized school programs. The child who builds a medieval castle at the insistence of his teacher and according to plans developed by the teacher gets little in the way of understanding. As a matter of fact, so far as understanding of life in medieval times is concerned, he might just about as well memorize a series of verbal statements in his textbook.

One further point concerning the relation between need and understanding should be made. Needs are of different sorts. Some of them grow out of meaningful and positive goals which pupils have; for example, the desire to build an airplane, to organize a club, to learn more and more about science, to prepare for medicine. Others are artificially injected into the child's life by parents and teachers and are often negative in character. Teachers may create needs through withholding approval, through denying privileges, through punishment; but the understanding which results from learning in response to such needs is likely to be of a low order.

In any given learning situation the teacher's purposes usually comprehend and frequently go beyond those of his pupils. On occasion the teacher expects, but does not secure, intelligent behavior in response to "problems" which he sets for his pupils. The anticipated behavior may not occur for a number of reasons. One reason, the one with which we are here concerned, is that the situation as arranged by the teacher arouses no feeling of need for such behavior on the part of the pupils. It follows that, in so far as intelligent behavior and the use and development of understandings are involved, teacher-purposes and pupil-purposes must always be made to harmonize.

b) To develop understanding the pupil must possess a background of relevant experience sufficient for the needs of the moment. The person who would understand a particular situation must bring to bear on it learning acquired in related but somewhat dissimilar situations. No teacher would expect students who cannot add whole numbers to understand the addition of the more abstract symbols of algebra; but the need for relevant experience is not always so obvious. Social-studies teachers who carry their pupils into a complicated analysis of Chinese culture prior to adequate experience in and analysis of their own immediate environment cannot expect much understanding as an outcome. Failure to observe this principle may often be traced to a misconception of the term "relevant experience." A child whose experience has been limited to the nature of a thing may not be in a position to deal successfully with processes which involve this thing. A child who has seen automobiles, even ridden in them, may not be ready to deal intelligently with the principles inherent in their operation.

c) To acquire understanding the pupil must focus his attention on the aspects or details of the situation which hold the key to understanding. A child may have experience over a long period of time with some situation and still get little understanding of it. Even as adults, after long familiarity we may get new "insights" from attending to something in a new way.

Teachers have an important role to play in assisting children to direct their attention to the critical aspects of a situation. Much of the economy accruing from supervised study comes from help given at this point. Habits of critical analysis, of classification, of seeing relationships, of identifying those that are cause-and-effect in nature, of arriving at sound generalizations, all processes involved in understanding, are susceptible to development under wise guidance.

d) Understanding increases when a pupil formulates the results of his learning in his own words and in various ways. One reason for the importance of self-evaluation in learning comes from the exercise it gives in identifying the desirable understandings which are implicit in an experience. Such formulations should, however, be in the nature of a rehearsal. Throughout any learning experience the teacher should encourage his pupils to verbalize, to talk about and write about the significant elements in the experience. And in so doing, it is well to keep in mind that exact reproduction of materials studied furnishes no additional understanding and offers no evidence of understanding. To accept such performances is but to condone rote learning.

e) To get understanding the pupil must make an active, aggressive approach to learning. Pupils must be encouraged to "discover" the things, processes, or relations of which understanding is sought. Most teachers talk too much. They are fearful of silence; they are unwilling to allow the learner the time necessary to muddle through. Oftentimes, too, our methods of presentation are such as to prevent personal discovery. Recognizing understanding of a certain principle in science as the desired outcome of instruction, for example, we too often start with it, define it, give our own illustrations, point out important ramifications, then (if there is time left) get a few additional illustrations out of the brighter members of the class. It is no accident that from such teaching the child often retains nothing more than the memory of a specific illustration.

f) Maximum understanding probably results when the teacher works in such a way that the pupil is allowed to participate actively and purposefully in planning what should be done at any given time, in the doing of it, and in evaluating success and failure. The teacher who dominates the learning situation to the extent of deciding exactly what will be done, and how much and when it will be done, and who, himself alone, passes judgment on the success attained can expect little real understanding to take place. This is true whether he dominates through force or fear, or through the more subtle device of clever salesmanship. It is the nature of understanding that very little of it results when pupils work for fear of the teacher or for love of the teacher, for fear of low grades, or for desire for high grades.

Understanding of a particular kind is most complete when the learner himself has had opportunity to make a choice and has come to the conclusion that such and such is the important thing to do. Contrawise, understanding is limited when some helper, whether it be the teacher or another pupil, does all the work for the learner. The teacher who conceives of himself as a "walking encyclopedia" or as a "trouble-shooter," who does for pupils the things which they cannot or do not want to do, can rest assured that a minimum of understanding will result from his teaching. A complaint often heard from mathematics teachers that pupils can't understand problems until they are read to them might be better phrased: They *won't* understand problems as long as their problems are read to them. And why should they, if the teacher is ready and willing to do it for them?

And, finally, it is in the area of evaluation that many of us err most. Traditionally, it has been the teacher's job to evaluate. The child writes a letter, works a problem, performs an experiment, cooks a meal, translates a French story—and the teacher passes judgment on the accomplishment. We who are teachers must come to see that successful understanding as well as maximum improvement comes from pupil participation at the point of evaluation.[12]

[12] William A. Brownell and Verner M. Sims, "The Nature of Understanding," in *The Measurement of Understanding*, Forty-fifth Yearbook of the National Society for the Study of Education, Part I (Chicago: University of Chicago Press, 1946), pp. 38-41.

Evaluation of Instruction

If we wish to determine whether a health instruction program is sound, we should find out the changes which have taken place in pupil understandings, attitudes, and practices as a result of the program. The results of a sound program of health instruction are reflected in desirable changes in the understandings, attitudes, and practices of children.

Because the desired outcomes in pupil behavior depend largely on content and method, the teacher is interested from time to time in determining the appropriateness of the content and the effectiveness of the methods in the health teaching program. She is particularly interested in such an evaluation when she wishes to correct weaknesses in the instructional program or when she wishes to experiment with other content and other methods which may prove more effective. Evaluation of a teaching program calls for a planned procedure. This procedure may be either informal or formal. The teacher recognizes that she has conducted an informal evaluation each time she decides to change even the smallest aspect of her teaching program in an attempt to make the program more effective. This kind of evaluation is a continuous process and is part of the teacher's daily experience in the classroom.

Periodically the teacher conducts a more formal type of evaluation. In the process of developing the health instruction program she has used specific criteria as a basis for choosing desired outcomes, content, and methods. When she decides to evaluate formally a part of the instructional program which seems relatively ineffective or when she wishes to experiment with the program as a whole, her plans call for a review of her original choices. Through the use of evaluating techniques (see Chap. 12) she discovers whether there is need for change in the desired outcomes, content, or methods of the teaching program. For example, she can determine by means of a check on the eating habits of children in her classroom whether the instructional program in nutrition is effective. The results of her inquiry may indicate a need for more emphasis on the proper choice of foods for the between-meal snack. The teacher is aware that the field of health instruction is dynamic. The content of the program must be changed periodically if it is to keep pace with technical advances in the broad field of health. Pupil participation in the evaluation of a health instruction program is desirable. The reactions of members of a class to the methods and the content of the instructional program should be encouraged. This reaction can be a valuable supplement to other information which the teacher obtains when she evaluates the health instruction program.

SELECTED REFERENCES

COMMISSION ON HEALTH IN SCHOOLS. *Health in Schools,* rev. ed. Twentieth Yearbook of the American Association of School Administrators. Washington, D. C.: National Education Association, 1951, pp. 142-63.

COMMITTEE ON THE RELATION OF EMOTION TO THE EDUCATIVE PROCESS, ch. Daniel A. Prescott. *Emotion and the Educative Process.* Washington, D. C.: American Council on Education, 1938.

COOPS, HELEN L. *Health Education in Elementary Schools.* New York: A. S. Barnes and Co., 1949.

GROUT, RUTH E. *Health Teaching in Schools,* 2d ed. Philadelphia: W. B. Saunders Co., 1953.

OBERTEUFFER, DELBERT. *School Health Education,* rev. ed. New York: Harper & Bros., 1954, Part II.

TURNER, CLAIR E. *School Health and Health Education.* St. Louis: C. V. Mosby Co., 1952.

WILSON, CHARLES C. (ed.). National Education Association and American Medical Association, Joint Committee on Health Problems in Education. *Health Education,* 4th ed. Washington, D. C.: National Education Association, 1948.

———. "Planning Together for Good Health," in *Health in the Elementary School.* Twenty-ninth Yearbook of the Department of Elementary School Principals, National Education Association. Washington, D. C.: National Education Association, 1950, pp. 12-26.

Chapter 9

THE PROGRAMS OF SAFETY EDUCATION AND PHYSICAL EDUCATION

MANY activities in the curriculum of the elementary school make a contribution to the health program for pupils. Safety education and physical education are noteworthy in this respect. In many elementary schools the activities of these two programs are the responsibility of the classroom teacher, sometimes with the periodic assistance of specialists in the two fields and sometimes without such assistance.

Safety Education

Accidents are the leading cause of death among children. More children between the ages of one and fourteen years meet death from accidents than from the five next ranking causes of death combined (see Table 9). The trends in

TABLE 9

CAUSES OF DEATH AMONG CHILDREN 1-14 YEARS OF AGE, 1950

Accidents	10,313	Poliomyelitis	862
Cancer	3,156	Gastritis, enteritis colitis	779
Pneumonia	2,821	Nephritis	726
Congenital malformations	2,014	Heart disease	673
Tuberculosis	1,263	Meningitis (nonmeningococcal)	510

SOURCE: National Safety Council, *Accident Facts* (Chicago: National Safety Council, 1953), p. 16.

deaths and death rates from accidents involving children of school age were downward between 1922 and 1953 (see Fig. 14). Although the long-term trend in the death rate

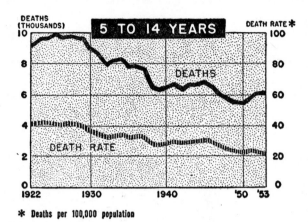

FIGURE 14. Trends in Deaths and Death Rates, 5- to 14-Year-Old Accident Experience. Source: National Safety Council, *Accident Facts* (Chicago: National Safety Council, 1954), p. 90.

from accidents is downward, the rate of reduction has been slow compared with that for other causes of death of children. The reason that the reduction in the death rate for accidents has not kept pace with the reduction in the death rate for other causes is clear. The tremendous reduction in the death rate for childhood communicable disease between the years 1900 and 1950 was due mainly to prevention of the spread of specific causative agents of disease; to immunization of individuals against specific diseases; to advances in medical, nursing, and hospital care; and to education of individuals in hygienic practices. Clearly, all the above procedures are not applicable to the problem of accident prevention. In general, safety education is limited to attempted control of environmental situations that might be provocative in causing accidents and to education of the individual which results in the kind of behavior that prevents accidents. Both of these procedures are reasonably well established in schools and much is expected from them. However, the fact remains that they do lack the comparative precision and finality of other procedures, such as successful immunization against diphtheria.

Responsibility for Education

A report of the National Safety Council[1] indicates the location of points where injuries to children take place (see Fig. 15). Sixty per cent are associated with school, and this

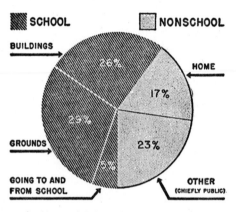

Source: Reports to the National Safety Council from school systems with enrollment of about 1,750,000 students

Injuries requiring the attention of a doctor, or causing absence from school of one-half day or more

FIGURE 15. Student Injuries, by Location. Source: National Safety Council, *Accident Facts* (Chicago: National Safety Council, 1953), p. 92.

fact suggests that attention should be given to hazards in the school environment and to hazards existing in the environment of the child while he is going to and from school. The report states that injuries on school grounds occurred somewhat more frequently during organized than during unor-

[1] *Accident Facts* (Chicago: National Safety Council, 1953), p. 92.

ganized activities and that about one-third of the injuries which occurred in school buildings took place in the gymnasium.[2]

Although the majority of reported accidents to children do occur in connection with school activities, the problem of safety education is not the sole responsibility of the school. The home and the community have responsibility both for control of the environment of the child and for his incidental education through supervision and guidance. The remaining 40 per cent of the points where injuries to children take place are not associated with school, but are associated with home or community (see Fig. 14). Even in the case of these injuries, the school has a certain responsibility because factors associated with personal behavior are involved and these factors are presumed to be capable of modification through education.

The same report of the National Safety Council tabulates accidents to students by type and grade level. The classroom teacher may find suggestions in this tabulation for emphasis in her safety education program (see Table 10).

Accidents—Environmental Factors

The basic causes of accidents may be classified under two headings, environmental factors and factors associated with personal behavior. It is often difficult to ascribe the primary cause of an accident to one factor only. In many instances, the cause is a combination of both environmental and personal factors, and deciding which factor played the primary and which the secondary role is sometimes difficult. An effective school safety program calls for the control of all causative factors in accidents. This suggests the elimination of all environmental hazards in school buildings and on school grounds and an educational program which is designed to control the human factors in the accident problem.

[2] *Ibid.*, p. 92.

TABLE 10

STUDENT ACCIDENTS BY TYPE AND GRADE, 1952-53

Location and Type	All Grades	Kgn.	1st	2nd	3rd	4th	5th	6th	7th	8th
SCHOOL JURISDICTION	100.0%	100.0%	100.0%	100.0%	100.0%	100.0%	100.0%	100.0%	100.0%	100.0%
School building	42.8%	37.7%	24.8%	24.4%	22.1%	25.8%	26.7%	29.4%	50.6%	51.2%
Classrooms and auditorium	8.0	25.8	12.7	9.9	9.3	8.5	8.2	6.7	8.7	7.5
Laboratories and dom. science	1.3	0	0	0	.1	.1	0	.4	2.0	1.7
Vocational shops	5.1	0	0	0	.1	.1	.3	.5	4.3	5.9
Gymnasium—basketball	6.3	0	.1	.1	.5	.7	1.7	2.1	6.1	7.8
—other	8.4	.1	.7	2.2	3.1	5.6	6.9	7.5	11.4	11.4
Swimming pool and showers	1.5	0	.1	.3	.1	.2	.6	.5	1.9	1.5
Dressing, washrooms, lockers	2.6	2.6	3.8	3.6	2.6	2.3	1.5	2.4	3.8	3.3
Corridors	3.5	3.2	3.2	3.4	2.4	3.3	2.9	2.9	4.5	4.6
Stairs and stairways	4.3	3.4	2.4	3.2	2.6	3.4	3.5	4.7	6.0	5.6
Other building accidents	1.8	2.6	1.8	1.7	1.3	1.6	1.1	1.7	1.9	1.9
School grounds	48.8%	47.4%	59.2%	61.4%	64.5%	62.6%	62.7%	61.5%	41.3%	41.7%
Apparatus—swings	.8	2.3	3.0	2.6	2.3	1.3	1.0	.8	.1	.1
—slides, teeters	1.3	8.1	5.8	3.2	3.2	1.9	1.5	.7	.2	.1
—bars	1.6	4.1	4.1	4.3	3.5	2.7	1.7	1.0	1.7	.8
—other	1.3	5.0	4.1	4.1	2.2	1.5	1.6	1.5	.5	.3

Athletics—baseball	4.4	.4	1.0	1.8	3.2	6.2	6.8	8.7	4.7	5.5
—football	10.0	0	.1	.4	.5	1.5	3.2	3.7	6.6	10.1
—soccer, track	2.0	0	.1	.1	.3	.8	1.6	1.2	2.6	3.3
Other organized activities	6.3	.8	1.9	4.7	8.3	11.1	15.4	15.5	4.8	5.3
Unorganized activities { running	5.7	8.4	11.8	13.2	13.4	11.1	7.9	7.5	4.7	3.6
scuffling	3.0	2.2	5.0	4.8	4.8	4.3	3.7	3.6	4.1	3.1
other falls	5.7	8.9	11.9	11.0	10.9	9.2	7.9	7.1	5.8	3.7
other	6.7	7.2	10.4	11.2	11.9	11.0	10.4	10.2	5.5	5.8
Going to or from School	8.4%	14.9%	16.0%	14.2%	13.4%	11.6%	10.6%	9.1%	8.1%	7.1%
Motor-vehicle accidents	2.8	8.3	6.8	5.6	3.6	3.1	2.3	2.2	2.0	2.2
Other accidents	5.6	6.9	9.2	8.6	9.8	8.5	8.3	6.9	6.1	4.9
School jurisdiction accident rate*	8.8	2.5	5.6	6.1	6.5	7.0	8.0	9.7	12.4	13.8

Based on reports of 26,643 school jurisdiction accidents from school systems with an average enrollment of 1,751,000. Accidents included are those requiring a doctor's attention or causing absence from school of one-half day or more.

* Rate is the number of accidents per 100,000 student days.

SOURCE: National Safety Council, Accident Facts (Chicago: National Safety Council, 1953), p. 93. Grades 9-12, unclassified students, and nonschool jurisdiction accidents are omitted.

An inclusive list of the immediate causes of accidents has been prepared by the Center for Safety Education of New York University, as follows:

Street and Highway Accidents

Lack of provision for safe play areas
Walking or playing in the roadway
Improper practices of adolescent drivers
Crossing against signals and between intersections, and jay-walking
Increased congestion of vehicles on highways
Drivers disregarding regulations and safe practices
Lack of safe practices in pupil transportation
Improper use of bicycles, scooters, and motorcycles
Failure to provide safe places for coasting

Accidents on School Premises

Faulty conditions or unsafe practices in school buildings
Unsafe apparatus, lack of supervision, or unsafe practices on playgrounds
Unsafe acts in school gymnasium and locker rooms
Unsafe practices in school shops and laboratories
Inadequate control of, or preparation for, competitive sports

Home Accidents

Carelessness leading to fires and burns
Unsafe storage of firearms and fireworks
Disorderliness and poor housekeeping leading to falls and other accidents
Careless use of external and internal poisons
Unsafe practices with gas

Accidents in Recreational Activities

Swimming and ice skating in unsupervised places
Lack of swimming and lifesaving skills
Improper use of boats and canoes
Unsupervised playground activities
Inadequate supervision during fishing, hiking, or camping trips
Unsafe practices with firearms and fireworks
Unsafe practices in nonschool play areas[3]

[3] New York University, Center for Safety Education, *The Administrator and the School Safety Program* (New York: New York Univ., 1953), p. 2.

Accidents—Human Factors

Certain human factors that contribute to accidents are associated with the physical condition of the individual. Defective vision or hearing loss, for example, can interfere with a child's awareness of important elements in a situation which may constitute hazards. Inability of an individual to judge distance or visual depth in a situation can be a principal cause in an accident. In similar fashion, inability to hear a warning bell or the noise incidental to an approaching vehicle can be a principal cause of accidents.

There are a certain number of children whose lack of coordination can be a cause predisposing to accident involvement. This may or may not be associated with constitutional characteristics which prescribe for the individual a tempo of movement that varies markedly from the one required in a specific situation.

In an unselected group of children some have a level of intelligence that is a limiting factor in understanding the school's program in safety education. For them, learnings that are designed to insure the type of behavior which avoids accidents must come in part from imitation of the desirable behavior of others. A comparison of children who are classified as *accident-susceptibles* (repeaters) with those who are classified as *accident-free* indicates a superior knowledge of safety in the latter group.

Teachers and parents are aware of the relationship between a transient fit of anger or an attitude of resentment or rebellion on the part of a child and a compulsive form of behavior that shows little regard for consequences. Evidence has been compiled which shows that emotional and social maladjustment is not uncommonly associated with a high accident rate. Other investigators consider that the area of psychomotor and sensory measures is a field which offers basic information about the cause of accidents.

The relationship of the physical characteristics of an individual and his emotional behavior to the frequency with which he is involved in accidents has resulted in the designation of some persons as *accident-susceptibles*. The accident-susceptible individual seems to possess a tendency to become involved in accidents (proneness toward accidents). Some investigators who work with adults and emphasize the psychiatric approach to the problem of accidents maintain that the majority of accidents result from subconsciously intended actions by individuals of certain personality types. Langford and others have done preliminary work in an attempt to determine the basic causes of children's accidents.

The purpose of [their] investigation was to explore methods for identifying and determining the significance, in relation to the incidence of accidents in children, of parental attitudes, parent-child relationships, environmental accident hazards, personality characteristics and functioning of the child, physical coordination and physical disabilities as these are reflected in the experience of the accident-repeater.[4]

Findings of this investigation, pertinent for the classroom teacher, are contained in the summary which follows. (It must be kept in mind that the number of cases in this study was small, and the findings should be used accordingly.)

The accident child in one group is over-active and restless. He tends to be impulsive. He is well liked by adults but not well liked by his fellows. He does not get his dependency and security satisfactions at home. He tends to want to be older than his age and to overextend himself in his activities as he tries to keep up with his ambitions or seek acceptance by the group. He does not retreat from dangerous situations. He has a poor reaction to stress, becoming more impulsive and disorganized. Some of the accidents occur during this stress disorganization. Under stress he does not recognize or heed

[4] William S. Langford *et al.*, "Pilot Study of Childhood Accidents: Preliminary Report," *Home Safety* (Publication of the National Safety Council, Chicago), XIII (1952), 4.

danger signals. As yet there has not seemed to be a specific type of situation which produces the disorganizing anxiety.[5]

The accident-repeater child described above would seem to get into situations where accidents were inevitable if he is under stress. The accidents then might well be unmotivated and the defect be a developmental one in the ego control mechanism.

In our accident patients we could see two other types of children, one related to immaturity, lack of parental supervision, an insistence on the part of the child on autonomy and self-determination, and competition in activities with older children in a hazardous environment.

The other typified by a resentful, hostile boy who views his home as bleak and empty, a boy who prior to his beginning to have accidents three years ago presented a moderately severe conduct disorder. As this has cleared, his general overt behavior has become resentful and rebellious. This boy does show pent up rage and aggression; he does salvage some attention from his mother when he is injured. These accidents may well be motivated. In a longer series of cases it is possible that even more personality types would emerge.[6]

The accident child seems to possess an inability to accept supervision in a situation of potential hazard. The non-accident child, on the other hand, seems to be less venturesome and to be more dependent on members of his family. He has established close relationship with members of his immediate family and is more submissive to authority.

Bases of Educational Program

Safety may well be characterized as a way of living, and as such, becomes an integral part of the life of an individual. The extent to which he has made it an integral part of his life is indicated by evidence of responsibility for his behavior as it concerns his own welfare and that of others.

In as much as people's *actions* or *failures to act* are dependent upon the knowledge, habits, attitudes, skills, and understandings which they possess, education for influencing these factors involves much more than merely teaching safety rules, "do's" and "don'ts," or what to do when the unexpected happens. The present trend in thinking is that

[5] *Ibid.*, p. 17.
[6] *Ibid.*, p. 18.

anything which we do for promoting an ability among our pupils to assume responsibility for their behavior is a part of safety education.[7]

Out of the ordinary activities of daily living arises the need for making choices between safe and unsafe action in situations which have within them the potential of injury to self or to others. For making these choices the child needs to acquire an understanding of the possible consequences of different types of behavior in a given situation and to have the ability to make the choice that will reduce the incidence of accidents to a minimum. It is equally important that the child have a *desire* to make choices in behavior that are based on his understanding of consequences. The child's desire and ability to make correct choices in behavior are strengthened by a teaching program that employs both the direct and the indirect methods of instruction.

Purposes and Objectives of Program

The broad purposes of a program of safety for the individual are—

1. To develop an awareness of the interdependence of individuals in daily living and a respect for the law and for the type of social behavior this interdependence requires.
2. To develop attitudes based on understandings and appreciations of the consequence of his behavior that will result in a sense of responsibility for himself and others.
3. To develop habits and skills in personal behavior that will produce consistently successful accomplishment and will prove the worth of intelligent and careful planning.

A list of school-wide pupil objectives, which the classroom teacher may find useful when she is developing units of work

[7] Tennessee Department of Education and Tennessee Department of Public Health, *Health Teaching, A Guide for Grades 1 Through 12* (Nashville: Tennessee Department of Education and Tennessee Department of Public Health, 1953), p. 87.

in safety, appears in a report by the Illinois Joint Committee on School Health. The child should—

Learn the extent of injuries and fatalities which occur yearly.

Realize that a majority of accidents can be prevented.

Learn the cause of and avoid accidents in the home, such as falls, burns, fires, poisoning, electrical shocks, and asphyxiation.

Learn the cause of and avoid automobile accidents, such as those occasioned by violating traffic regulations, stealing rides, getting on or off moving vehicles, and careless pedestrian habits.

Learn the cause of and avoid accidents while playing, such as those occasioned by the improper handling of fireworks and firearms or taking unnecessary risks while swimming, boating, coasting, or skating.

Learn and practice the rules of safe conduct in the use of school buildings, gymnasiums, playgrounds, and athletic fields.

Learn and develop habits of safe conduct in occupational activities in which pupils frequently participate in addition to attending school.

Learn safe ways of meeting the common hazards associated with the occupations with which a majority of the pupils are likely to be associated in adult life.

Develop habits and attitudes which will enable the individual to meet situations of daily life with the least possible risk, exposure, and danger.

Develop coordination, alertness, strength, and agility as a means of avoiding accidents.

Learn the value of cooperation for the protection of all.

Learn and realize the futility of taking unnecessary risks involving added chances for accidents.

Develop wholesome attitudes in regard to risk, safe practices, and safety rules and regulations.

Develop a respectful and wholesome attitude toward persons charged with the duty of providing and maintaining safe working and living conditions.

Gain experience in numerous safety practices.

Create, develop, and maintain an active interest in the protection of life and property in the community.

Develop a sense of responsibility for the safety of others in all situations.

Learn the theory and practice of first aid.

Learn to apply the scientific knowledge gained in school subjects for the safety and welfare of the individual and the group.

Assist in developing safe conditions for work and play as an important part of community life.[8]

The Instructional Program

The development of competencies which result in accident-free living is furthered by making provision in the school program for actual experiences in desirable behavior practices. It is particularly important, however, to distinguish between the kind of experiences that have potential for the development of skills and those that can have catastrophic results for the child. Against the latter, protection is called for in school, home, and community. This does not mean complete avoidance of the type of venturesome activity which, when successful, brings with it a satisfying sense of accomplishment, and even when unsuccessful, may result in a desirable learning experience. There is substantial educative value in the minor mishaps of childhood. Dietrich expresses an interesting point of view in reference to childhood accidents.

If we consider accident prevention in the terms of any other immunization procedure, we must acknowledge that *protection* affords only passive immunity. As such it is effective for very limited periods of time if it is supplied in adequate dosage. *Education* provides active immunity against accidents; it is relatively slow in achieving clinically effective titers, and must be given in repeated booster doses.[9]

The education which is referred to by Dietrich should result in gradually increasing self-direction by the individual

---

[8] Illinois Joint Committee on School Health, *A Basic Plan for Health Education and the School Health Program* (Springfield, Illinois: State Department of Education, 1944), pp. 22-23.

[9] Harry F. Dietrich, M.D., "Clinical Application of the Theory of Accident Prevention in Childhood," *American Journal of Public Health*, XLII (1952), 852-53.

and should enable him to protect himself and others more effectively.

A well-arranged program of experiences in health education has been prepared by the Division of Instructional Services of the Los Angeles City School Districts. This guide, from which a problem in safety education has been chosen as an illustration, represents cooperative endeavor of school, home, and community (see Table 11).

Another well-organized plan of instruction in safety education is found in the manual *Safety Education (Elementary Level)*, published by the Maine State Department of Education. "Safety at Home and on the Farm" (intermediate grade level) illustrates the instructional material found in this manual (see Table 12).

An excellent instrument for making a school safety program effective is the school safety committee. Representation on the committee is the result of nomination and election by pupils. The activities of committee members are guided by the faculty member responsible for the school safety program. Usually, the activities of this committee are determined after a survey of safety problems has been made (see pp. 164-66). This survey may be carried on by the safety committee, but can be more effective and has more educational value when all pupils in the school take part. Cooperation with community agencies is not required for the solution of most of the problems that become evident as a result of a survey. However, such cooperation is necessary for the solution of some problems. For example, problems that involve pedestrian safety, as when pupils walk to and from school, or those that involve bicycle safety require cooperation between the school safety committee, the home, and the local safety council or safety division of the police department.

TABLE 11

PROBLEM: HOW CAN CHILDREN LEARN SAFE WAYS TO RIDE IN A
CAR, BUS, OR STREETCAR?

Possible Attainments

Growth in Knowledge:	The children learn that safety precautions in the use of vehicles prevent accidents.
Growth in Attitudes:	The children realize that bus drivers are concerned with their safety, but that they too have responsibilities.
Growth in Practices:	The children try to help make riding in a car, bus or streetcar easier and safer for everyone.

Experiences of Children

Visiting and Discussing:

In many schools children use school buses for daily transportation. In one such school a teacher and her class made arrangements with the bus driver to visit his bus. With the driver's help all the children boarded the bus in the safe way. When they were seated inside, they discussed all phases of bus safety. The driver told them that he wanted to prevent anyone from being hurt. He explained how each safety rule protects the passengers.

Demonstrating and Helping:

The visit ended with a demonstration of getting off buses safely. When the children reached their classroom, they were quite agreed that they too wanted to prevent accidents.

In order that they should not forget the safety practices they had discussed on the bus, they listed the ones they thought were important, as follows:

Keep your arms and head inside the vehicle.

Avoid disturbing the driver by loud talking because accidents are more apt to happen on a noisy than on a quiet bus.

Wait on the curb for a bus and stay there until the bus door opens.

Wait until it is safe to cross the street before boarding a bus, and after leaving it.

Hold the handrail while getting off a bus or streetcar.

Face forward when getting off.

Remain seated at all times when riding on bus or streetcar unless required to stand; then face the side of the bus or car, spread your feet apart, and grasp the handgrips.

TABLE 11 (*continued*)

Those who rode to school in private cars said that almost all the rules fit them too. They added to the list:

Avoid touching door handles when riding in private cars.

Always get in and out of cars on the side away from traffic.

The children worked out a plan whereby those who rode the bus daily had an opportunity periodically to report to the group the particular things they were doing to promote safety. The bus driver commented later about a marked improvement in bus behavior.

Listing and Discussing: One group was planning a class trip on a school bus. They set up their own standards for safe behavior. When their list was complete they compared it with the rules developed by the Transportation Division. These rules were made following a study of accidents on buses. The children discovered a few items which they had not included on their list. Two of them were, "No singing" and "No eating on bus." They discussed how such behavior could cause accidents and added them to their standards.

Instructional Materials

Film Strips: The Field Trip
Leaflets: Driving Your Child to School (for parents) Automobile Club of Southern California
Posters: Automobile Club of Southern California
Books Available in Sets: Health Through the Year (Grade 3) pp. 73, 124-125.
The Girl Next Door (Grade 4) pp. 217-220.
Health at Work and Play (Grade 5) pp. 38-42.
Building Good Health (Grade 6) pp. 236-237.

SOURCE: Los Angeles City School Districts, Division of Instructional Services, *Experiences in Health Education for Elementary School Children,* Publication No. 566 (Los Angeles: Los Angeles City School Districts, 1953), pp. 141-43.

TABLE 12
SAFETY AT HOME AND ON THE FARM

Home accidents resulting in death closely parallel those for which traffic is responsible. Total injuries from the same source are four times as great. The greater part of these casualties are due to unsafe conditions and practices in the home.

Elementary school children are not too young to receive instruction in safe home living. This is the job of the classroom teacher. However, the home economics teacher, trained in this area, is always available for help and guidance in planning activities which will satisfy the needs of boys and girls in this area.

PROBLEMS	ACTIVITIES
Avoiding home accidents	Discuss some causes of home accidents and how to prevent or remedy them: Broken steps, loose rugs, wiring, defective cords, poorly lighted stairs, blocked passages, improper storage, disorder, careless handling of guns, fire hazards, and slippery floors.
	Arrange a display of pictures, posters, and newspaper clippings showing causes and results of home accidents.
	Use materials from National Safety Council and life insurance companies in regard to where and how accidents happen.
	Discuss home accidents that have occurred in own home and in the community during the past few years.
	Study the relationship of disorder in the home to accidents.
Preventing self-caused accidents	Prepare an exhibit on home safety for a store window or for a prominent place at school.
	Show a film on "safety first."
	Discuss gasoline and cleaning fluids as fire hazards.
	Demonstrate removing lid from steaming kettle, right way to strike matches, deep fat frying and lighting a gas oven.
	Demonstrate ways of anchoring small rugs.
	Collect or draw cartoons showing lack of home safety.
Avoiding accidents through carelessness of others	Decide on changed practice that would increase the safety of a family.
	Plant safety hazards in a school room or home and have pupils compete for the number they recognize.
	Keep bulletin board of clippings on accidents.

TABLE 12 *(continued)*

Protecting younger members of the family	Plan for and make cupboards for children's toys and clothing.
	Report on accidents which are common among children and discuss their prevention.
	Dramatize some "safety first" ideas for assembly.
	Have each member of the class work on one problem needing attention to make his home safe.
Learning what to do in case of accident in school or industry	Study simple first-aid measures, good antiseptics, gauze, tape.
	Read safety rules used by industry.
Learning what to do in case of accident in the home	Present skit showing proper way to call fire department. Have local fire chief speak on how to turn in alarm and what to do until firemen come.
Using different knives or scissors with least danger of injury	List kinds of cutting accidents.
	Practice using knives safely.
Recognizing "sharp" and "dull" tools	Discuss storage of tools.
	Make devices for safe storage.
	Sharpen knives.
Caring for cuts	Discuss care of common cuts.
Caring for electric cords	Ask pupils to bring in examples of dangerous cords.
	Demonstrate and practice repairing cords.
	Practice changing a fuse.
	Seek speaker or demonstrator from local power company.
Repairing furniture	Discuss fire hazard of paint removers and oily rags.
	Demonstrate good practices in refinishing furniture.

CHECKLIST FOR STUDENTS	YES	NO
Do we walk barefooted in dark?		
Do we leave toys on stairways?		
Do we use ladders with loose rungs?		

TABLE 12 (*continued*)

	YES	NO

Do we have magic carpets—loose rugs on polished floors?

Do we leave rakes, hoes, etc., lying on ground with cutting edges up?

Do we store tools in high places securely fastened?

Do we lift heavy objects without help?

Do we use dull tools?

Do we inspect a gun which was not supposed to be loaded?

Does anyone smoke in bed at home?

Do we repair electrical appliances and wiring without experience?

Do we use cleaning fluids in vicinity of an open fire?

Do handles of pans with hot liquids extend out from stove?

Do we avoid running up and down stairs, sliding down banisters?

Do we use rocking chairs for ladders?

Do we keep away from open wells and cisterns?

Do we keep away from the medicine cabinet?

Do we know how to put out a clothing fire?

Do we avoid touching loose wires and notify adults?

Work Projects
  Survey home for safety equipment used.
  Study building codes and fire protection of your locality.
  Study farm building practices to improve safety.

Evidences of Pupil Growth
  Understands falls occur when objects are strewn around.
  Knows how to disconnect electric appliances safely.
  Knows it is dangerous to handle electrical appliances if feet
    and hands are wet.
  Secures first-aid for injuries, no matter how trivial.
  Is cautious about handling hot liquids.
  Knows how to make safety inspection of the home.

SOURCE: State of Maine Department of Education, *Safety Education* (*Elementary Level*), Curriculum Bulletin No. 16 (Augusta: State of Maine Department of Education, 1952), pp. 48-51.

A good method for evaluating the effectiveness of a school's program in safety education is found in *Experiences in Health Education for Elementary School Children:*

STANDARDS FOR A SCHOOL SAFETY EDUCATION PROGRAM

This outline was prepared by national authorities in safety education to serve as criteria for judging accident prevention programs in elementary schools. It makes an interesting check sheet for evaluating a program in safety education.

I. Provided safety instruction to meet the needs of the pupils; needs to be determined by:
   A. Analysis of the temporary and permanent hazards of the environment.
   B. Analysis of the hazards in connection with the activities of the pupils.
   C. Analysis of the records collected through the standard student accident reporting system.
   D. Analysis of the hazards of the seasons and of special days, such as Halloween, Christmas, Fourth of July.
   E. Consideration of individual pupil problems.

II. Provided for the active participation of pupils in caring for their own safety; for example:
   A. Pupil safety organizations (Junior Safety Councils, School Safety Patrols, Student Safety Committees, School Building Helpers, Monitors, Bicycle Clubs, etc.).
   B. Pupil formulation and evaluation of rules for action.
   C. Pupil inspections.

III. Utilized instructional aids for a well-rounded program of school, recreation, traffic, fire, and home safety; for example:
   A. Text material (books, lesson units, work sheets).
   B. Audio-Visual aids (motion pictures, film strips, slides, posters).
   C. Models.
   D. Pupil-made materials.

IV. Provided realistic opportunities for supervised practice in meeting hazards; for example:
   A. Crossing streets.
   B. Using school equipment (pencils, scissors, saws, stoves, slides, swings, etc.).
   C. Using transportation system.
   D. Fire drills.

V. Kept safety in the forefront of pupil-teacher-parent consciousness; for example:
   A. Exhibits and bulletin boards.

B. Slides or drawings of accident statistics.
C. Posters and other art work.
D. Assemblies, radio broadcasts or television shows.
E. School and community newspapers.
F. Spot maps of accident locations and safe walking routes.
G. Home or community inspection.[10]

Physical Education

The school program of physical education in the United States probably received its major impetus shortly after World War I. The findings of selective service boards, which had responsibility for enforcing the selective service Draft Statute of World War I, showed that many young men who were called for military service were not good physical specimens. Although many of the deficiencies were of the kind which could be remedied by medical attention only, the opinion seemed to be held generally that a more comprehensive program of physical education was called for. To meet the demands which were voiced, requirements that were gradually established on the state level called for specific time allotments for physical education in the curriculum of public schools. At present forty-two states have legislation relating to their elementary school program.[11]

Physical education in its early years in this country was modeled after the programs or systems of certain European countries. The primary purpose of such programs in these countries was to produce good physical specimens, capable of becoming good soldiers. Following the European pattern, the systems of physical education in this country

[10] Los Angeles City School Districts, Division of Instructional Services, *Experiences in Health Education for Elementary School Children*, Publication No. 566 (Los Angeles: Los Angeles City School Districts, 1953), pp. 161-62.

[11] Ralph W. Leighton and Lloyd H. Falgren, *An Analysis of Physical Education Legislation Applying to Public Schools of the Forty-Eight States* (Eugene, Ore.: School of Health and Physical Education, University of Oregon, 1950), Chart I.

during the middle and latter part of the nineteenth century were well grounded in formal gymnastics. Not until the turn of the century was the emphasis in physical education redirected from formal gymnastics toward the type of games program emphasized today.

The games type of program is more in keeping with the basic tendencies of the individual. A normal, healthy child seems to enjoy participation in games requiring big-muscle activity. Under properly controlled conditions this experience, which results in a heightened metabolic rate, seems to be desirable for a growing biological organism. There are other benefits which accrue from this program and which are influential in molding the personality of the growing child. The development of skills through which a sense of accomplishment is experienced and a gradual development of the art of adjusting to the personalities of others while engaged in common endeavor are reasonable outcomes to expect from a well-organized and well-conducted program of physical education. Such outcomes are not necessarily unique to physical education. They may result from other constructive experiences which are part of the school curriculum. What is unique in a program of physical education when compared to other programs in the school curriculum is the appeal it has to children and the enthusiasm of the normal healthy child for the program. This enthusiasm, which is the expression of a basic predisposition of the child toward physical activity, does hold unusual educational opportunities for the program in physical education. His interest in the program is easily established and the basic urge to excel, which most children have, finds ready opportunity for expression.

Purposes of Program

Some school administrators and others hold an opinion that a program in physical education is mainly a health program and that the purposes and the outcomes of such a program result *primarily* in an improvement in the health of individual pupils. Participation in physical activity does not insure against organic ailments nor is it a means of preventing infection. There is no known end-result of physical education that protects a person against a communicable disease.

Enthusiasts working in the field of physical education have occasionally claimed extensive benefits to pupils taking part in the physical education program and have implied that the outcomes are unique to physical education. Health improvement, character development, social adjustment have been mentioned. Actually, this program seems to have more justification for its existence because it can result, if properly conducted, in a muscularly efficient organism and one that is well-coordinated in reference to game skills. In the process of taking part in physical activity the whole organism is engaged at a higher rate of physiologic response than when resting. The structure and the normal functions of a healthy child are usually improved under these conditions.

It may be well to point out, however, that many structurally sound and adequately functioning children are not dependent on organized physical activity for their physiologic well-being. It is equally desirable to point out that standards of fair play and good sportsmanship are not the inevitable outcomes of organized activities in physical education nor are such desirable traits limited to those skilled in athletic accomplishment. Ideals, concepts of desirable behavior, and good group behavior can, and to a large extent, do have their origins in the home, in other personal contacts, and in other experiences which the individual may have.

Some of the commonly stated purposes of a program in physical education include:

Chapter 10

THE ROLE OF THE TEACHER IN MENTAL HEALTH

CERTAIN basic aims of education and mental hygiene are essentially the same, but too often the methods employed in educational practice seem to make little if any contribution to the mental health of the individual. In our schools we are or should be concerned with enabling the individual to develop into a well-rounded personality and to be capable of deep-felt happiness as a result of the interchange between himself and his environment. In too many instances, however, marked emphasis is placed on educational goals which have more concern for the academic accomplishments of the individual than for his emotional development.

In the pursuit of happiness in its broadest meaning, the individual learns of necessity to adjust to changing conditions in his environment at one time and to shape the conditions of his environment at another. To the extent that he succeeds, his life is free from the tensions and the strains that interfere with his effectiveness and mar his happiness. He becomes effective in his adjustment to varying conditions, and his relationships with other individuals are a source of lasting satisfaction.

Promotion of Mental Health

Many of the basic patterns of behavior that produce happiness are learned in childhood—particularly the patterns which involve relationships with other individuals. Consequently, school experiences become basically important in the establishment of desirable emotional attitudes and fundamental behavior patterns. These experiences comprise for the child a large part of his life, and his adjustment to school living is for him adjustment to life. Although the activities of the classroom may impress an adult as artificial and purposeless, they are to the child some of the most important experiences of everyday living.

A school situation contributes to the emotional development of pupils whenever relationships among school personnel insure smooth-working arrangements and whenever both understanding of the child and showing respect for his personality characterize the educational practices of the classroom.

Responsibility of Teacher

The teacher's first responsibility is to insure that the atmosphere of the classroom promotes the development of desirable personality traits. The "way of life" in her classroom reflects to a large extent her concept of the best ways of meeting the problems of life. Life in the classroom is a large part of the life of the child. The fair, reasonable, happy, and considerate teacher who brings genuine enthusiasm to her work establishes an atmosphere in her classroom which results in like behavior of her pupils. Some of the techniques she uses are well described in the statement which follows:

The teacher interested in the mental health of his pupils recognizes their desire for feelings of security. He sees to it that each pupil's special abilities are known to the group. He develops cooperative undertakings in which each pupil makes a significant, worthwhile contribution; he provides opportunities for pupils to experience the joy and happiness which are the birthright of children. Tasks are assigned which, tho challenging, carry a reasonable opportunity for successful completion, because the teacher is aware of the stimulating effect of success and the inhibiting power of constant or repeated failure. Fear, because of its detrimental psychological effect, is not used as a motivating factor. Pupils are given as much freedom as is consistent with the best interests of the group, and are helped to find ways of meeting the demands of security, self-respect, and activity that lead to cooperative behavior. In these various ways the teacher respects the personalities of pupils, thus helping them to develop self-respect and self-confidence. In a friendly, sympathetic manner he leads them toward increased independence, greater resourcefulness, and well-rounded growth. They develop a feeling of belonging to a group and feelings of security and happiness. They grow emotionally as well as intellectually and physically.[1]

Need for Understanding Child Behavior

The classroom teacher who has real concern for the mental health of her children is keenly aware that the teaching program cannot ignore the developmental needs and the desires of the group in her classroom. The older elementary age group, for example, has fundamental urges that require recognition of each as an individual. The child desires to be useful and important, and the associated problem of adjusting to authority sometimes becomes acute. Authority of the autocratic kind, which to the child seems oppressive, may result in rebellion. The classroom teacher knows that in this problem of adjustment lies for some the source of emotional disturbance. Respect for authority must be learned, but the manner in which the child is conditioned to it may well determine the success of the procedure. The Department of Child Guidance of the City of Newark, New Jersey, has prepared an excellent statement about the child's adjustment to school:

In adjusting to school, the child is making three of the fundamental adjustments to life. In the first place, he is making the social adjustment, that is, the adjustment to his classmates. In the family group,

[1] Commission on Health in Schools, *Health in Schools*, Twentieth Yearbook of the American Association of School Administrators (rev. ed.; Washington, D. C.: National Education Association, 1951), p. 126.

each child has his own individual relationship with the parents. Each child has his own rights. In school he is confronted with his contemporaries, thirty, forty, or fifty strong, all of whom have the same rights, and equal claims for recognition. The social world of his contemporaries is the one in which he is going to live. How can the school help him meet this competition without developing feelings of inferiority and resentment of other children?

In the second place, he is making an adjustment to authority. Often the school offers the child his only opportunity to form a healthy conception of authority, to see it, not as a blind force to which he must meekly submit, not as a hostile one, cruel and unfair, against which he secretly or openly rebels, but as a force which is just and friendly, essential for happy group living.

In the third place, the child learns in school to adjust to his own limitations. Every child, consciously or unconsciously, would like to be first, the brightest and best loved in every situation. Early in life he is apt to discover that he has limitations which prevent his reaching that goal. The school is in a position to help him find compensations through a wise use of what abilities he has, to encourage him to develop to a maximum within his own limits, and to build up in him such a reassuring sense of his own adequacy that he will be able to allow others to be superior, without himself feeling inferior.[2]

The successful teacher is primarily concerned with the general welfare of the children in her classroom. She understands the basic reasons for their behavior. She is sensitive to the wide differences in personality make-up among the children in her classroom, but respects the personality of the child although he is different from the majority. This fundamental requirement for success in teaching is well expressed by Carroll:

The child needs to have his abilities, whether small or great, recognized by his teacher and by his classmates. Some few individuals obtain full satisfaction from the knowledge that they have done well, but most persons desire that their contemporaries recognize their achievements. It enhances their feeling of personal worth. The desire for status does not necessarily mean that the individual expects to be

[2] Department of Child Guidance of the City of Newark, New Jersey, *Mental Hygiene in the Classroom* (New York: National Committee for Mental Hygiene, Inc., 1949), pp. 5-6.

outstanding. What he needs is the feeling that others like and respect him for what he is. The teacher who understands this emotional need will be as pleased with the minor classroom contributions as with the major ones. In class discussions she will encourage the dull and diffident student as much as the bright and confident one. She will not scorn the offer of the single talent because it is not ten times greater. She will never try to make any student in her class feel insignificant. She will be more lavish with praise than with criticism. She will help every student to maintain his self-respect.[3]

Adaptation of Classroom Programs

We are well aware that in every nonselected group of school children there is a wide variation in mental ability. Some members of the group are capable of academic accomplishment far in excess of others in the group and in excess of the demands made upon them by grade placement. Such pupils are in danger of acquiring undesirable attitudes toward work because of the lack of challenge due to the ease of accomplishing work assignments. At the other end of the scale are pupils for whom strictly academic accomplishment will always be denied. For them the competition in this area is too much, the race is unequal, and continued failure results only in feelings of frustration. In the process of adjustment called for in this situation the teacher can be a powerful influence on the child. Her own attitude toward the problems of the child and toward the child with problems can be instrumental in helping the child to develop healthy attitudes toward many of the ordinary occurrences of daily living.

If consideration for the emotional welfare of the pupil is taken into account, adaptations must be made in the curriculum of the school for meeting the various mental abilities of pupils. Such adaptations are important in the development of a sound preventive program in mental health. The

[3] Herbert A. Carroll, *Mental Hygiene, The Dynamics of Adjustment,* Second Edition (copyright, 1947, 1951, by Prentice-Hall, Inc.), p. 307. Reprinted by permission of the publisher.

role of the teacher is to consult with the school administrator, or as a committee member to contribute to recommendations about curriculum change. The final decision about curriculum change and about methods for determining pupil potential rests with the school administrator. However, the teacher has constructive suggestions about these problems and others which concern program enrichment for the superior pupil, modification of the program for the less accomplished, techniques of testing, and pupil placement.

Assistance for the Emotionally Disturbed Child

Even with good practices in curriculum adaptation, some pupils demonstrate types of behavior that are indicative of poor adjustment. Schools have a responsibility for these pupils, and this responsibility rests largely with the classroom teacher. She should be informed on the types of behavior which are regarded as important signs of poor adjustment. With this information she is able to recognize the child who has special need for her attention or who should be referred to a specialist in the field of guidance. Emotionally disturbed children usually give evidence of their disturbance in the daily activities of the classroom. Some of the common symptoms of maladjustment in school children are listed by Wheatley (see Table 14).

Recognition of Emotional Disturbance

In her observation of pupils the teacher is not diagnosing but is observing types of behavior. She is in a most advantageous position to learn of any emotional disturbances that may develop and to become aware of a child's feelings about the various relationships that make up his world of contacts. She is aware that children pass through various stages of personality development and that behavior appropriate to one stage may be undesirable at another. In the procedure of identifying cases of emotional and social maladjustment she

TABLE 14

SOME COMMON INDICATIONS OF MALADJUSTMENT IN SCHOOL CHILDREN

Attacking behavior	Temper outbursts Aggressiveness, defiant attitude, resistance to authority, disobedience Quarrelsomeness, fighting, boasting Rejection of school routine; wanting always to be the leader in school activities or to pursue own methods of work Contentiousness; poor sportsmanship Overactivity Delinquency, truancy
Withdrawing behavior	Shyness, timidity, cowardliness Unsocialness, solitariness, inability to make friends Dreaminess Extreme docility, overdependence on adults or on routine Sensitiveness to criticism, feelings easily hurt Pedantry, overdiligence in schoolwork Inability to carry responsibility
Somatic manifestations	Nail biting Finger sucking Pencil chewing Blinking Facial twitching Infantile speech Unestablished toilet habits
Educational problems	Difficulty with reading despite normal intelligence and vision Difficulties with arithmetic Lack of application Speech difficulties

SOURCE: By permission from *Health Observation of School Children, A Guide for Helping Teachers and Others to Observe and Understand the School Child in Health and Illness,* by George M. Wheatley and Grace T. Hallock, p. 142. Copyright, 1951, by McGraw-Hill Book Company, Inc., New York.

knows the general kind of behavior which may be expected from her own grade group. It is most important that she learn to look beyond immediate behavior for the explanation of a disturbed condition.

The teacher must also keep in mind the fact that the difficult personality traits and behavior of the child are not due to any mysterious dispensation but are the logical outcome of the life experiences of that individual and can be traced with fair clearness back through the years to their causes. The child's difficulties do not suddenly and perversely happen out of a clear sky. They usually have a long, intricate history extending into the past, in which the careful observer may discern the sequence of cause and effect. Thus, the path of understanding will require a greater expenditure of time and effort in patient inquiry than does the method of trial and punishment, but the constructive results flowing from the former method are incalculably greater.[4]

Continued misbehavior is an expression of hidden maladjustment and is a purposive, though misguided, attempt on the part of the child to obtain a measure of satisfaction in his daily living.

Role of Teacher in Adjustment

In her attempt to find out why the child behaves as he does, the teacher who approaches the problem analytically wants information about the child which she has not previously acquired in her classroom. The school nurse is able to supply information about the physical condition of the child, for example. Comprehensive information on this point may show the presence of an irritating condition such as a vision defect. This can be the source of nervous instability which in turn can predispose to undesirable patterns of behavior. The teacher also determines whether the child is intellectually capable of meeting the requirements of his grade placement. Evidence that the academic demands are too difficult for him suggests to the observant teacher a possible cause of his undesirable behavior.

Inquiry into only the physical status and the intellectual potential of the child does not satisfy the teacher who is intent on getting at the basic causes of poor adjustment.

[4] Clara Bassett, "The Teacher's Approach to the Problem Child," *National Education Association Journal*, XIX (1930), 242.

She is aware that the child has a life distinct from that spent under the direct influence of the school. The long association with members of his immediate family and with the emotional atmosphere of his home has helped to mold his personality. His feelings about his home and about events and practices in the community in which he lives may shed some light on the reasons for his behavior.

Where the services of a consulting psychologist, a psychiatrist, or a child guidance clinic are available, the teacher is concerned mainly with the screening and the referral of children in need of such services, and with the cooperative activity with such sources when recommendations are made that involve school procedure. For the teacher to whom such services are not available, there are obvious limitations in her work with a maladjusted child. Not all cases of emotionally disturbed children can be cared for by the school. Many times the home and local agencies take responsibility with the school playing a cooperative part. Because the public school is so intimately associated with the life of the child and is assuming more and more responsibility for all aspects of the development of children, the work of detection and of follow-up in cases of the emotionally maladjusted is properly in the province of the school.

Unfortunately, the behavior of the maladjusted child too often produces action of a disciplinary nature by the teacher. The power of her position is used to prevent the activity and to thwart the immediate purposes of the child. An analysis of the behavior of the troublesome child usually provides evidence that his actions are purposive and that his aim is part of an attempt to compensate for something that is unsatisfactory in his life.

The classroom teacher is not expected to assume the duties and the responsibilities of the psychiatric-social worker. The teacher's work is largely preventive in her procedures with the class as a whole, but she cooperates with the visiting teacher in work with individual pupils. In smaller schools where the services of a visiting teacher are not available, the classroom teacher is called upon to work directly with individual pupils.

Mental Health of the Teacher

The personality of the teacher is a powerful factor in the behavior reactions of the children in her charge. Just as the atmosphere of a school reflects in large part the attitude of the school administrator, so the atmosphere of the classroom reflects the personality of the teacher. Fears, frustrations, and other disturbed emotional conditions should not be allowed to influence the emotional tone of a classroom. The American Association of School Administrators has taken a firm position regarding the emotionally disturbed teacher in the classroom:

> The teacher with an uncontrollable temper, or one who is severely depressed, markedly prejudiced, flagrantly intolerant, bitingly sarcastic, or habitually scolding, may endanger the emotional health of pupils as seriously as one with tuberculosis or some other communicable disease endangers their physical health. Such a teacher needs help; but while he is being helped it is often advisable for him to be away from his classroom so that his pupils are free from the repression and fear which his presence creates.[5]

In her concern for her happiness and professional success, the teacher is aware that good physical health is necessary and plans periodic health appraisal for herself. She is also aware that good mental health is furthered by the cultivation of interests outside her chosen profession. Friendship with persons in other fields, the development of hobbies and active participation in community activities, for example, broaden the interests of the teacher. In addition, she may need to develop a feeling of adequacy in her work and a

[5] Commission on Health in Schools, *op. cit.*, p. 126.

sense of humor which relieves the occasional tension of teaching.

SELECTED REFERENCES

AMERICAN COUNCIL ON EDUCATION, COMMISSION ON TEACHER EDUCATION. *Helping Teachers Understand Children.* Washington, D. C.: American Council on Education, 1945.

CARROLL, HERBERT A. *Mental Hygiene, The Dynamics of Adjustment,* 2d ed. New York: Prentice-Hall, Inc., 1951.

COMMISSION ON HEALTH IN SCHOOLS. *Health in Schools,* rev. ed. Twentieth Yearbook of the American Association of School Administrators, National Education Association. Washington, D. C.: American Association of School Administrators, 1951, pp. 119-41.

Fostering Mental Health in Our Schools. 1950 Yearbook of the American Association for Supervision and Curriculum Development, National Education Association. Washington, D. C.: American Association for Supervision and Curriculum Development, 1950.

JACOBS, LOUIS. "Mental Health in the School Health Program," *Journal of School Health,* XXIII (March, 1953), 79-86.

MIDCENTURY WHITE HOUSE CONFERENCE ON CHILDREN AND YOUTH. *Personality in the Making.* New York: Harper & Bros., 1952.

NATIONAL EDUCATION ASSOCIATION AND AMERICAN MEDICAL ASSOCIATION, Joint Committee on Health Problems in Education. *Mental Hygiene in the Classroom.* Chicago: American Medical Association, 1949.

NEWMAN, HELEN C., M.D. "Mental Hygiene in the Classroom," *Journal of School Health,* XXIV (October, 1954), 207-14.

O'SULLIVAN, ALICE. "A Suggested Team Approach to School Mental Health," *Journal of School Health,* XXII (January, 1952), 11-17.

THORMAN, GEORGE. *Toward Mental Health,* 8th ed. (Public Affairs Pamphlet No. 120.) New York: Public Affairs Committee, 1950.

Chapter 11

SCHOOL AND COMMUNITY
RELATIONSHIPS

ALTHOUGH the school health program is commonly administered by the board of education, it should be considered part of the larger, more comprehensive community health program. Included in the community health program are (1) the activities of the official health agency, i.e., the department of health, which as a function of government is supported by taxation, and (2) the programs of the unofficial (voluntary) health agencies which are supported by endowment and by voluntary financial contributions. There are occasions when the schools are able to use advantageously the resources of both the official agency and the unofficial health agencies. An example of this cooperation is in the tuberculosis prevention program in which the schools, the official health agency, and the tuberculosis agency all take part. Each carries out the part of the program which it is best qualified to do.

Official Health and Welfare Departments

When the total school health program is the responsibility of the board of education, the resources of the board of health are available through cooperative activity. When the school health services program is a responsibility of the city or the county board of health, the entire resources of the board are available for school work.

Services of Health Department

These resources are indicated in an inspection of the services supplied by an official department of health (see

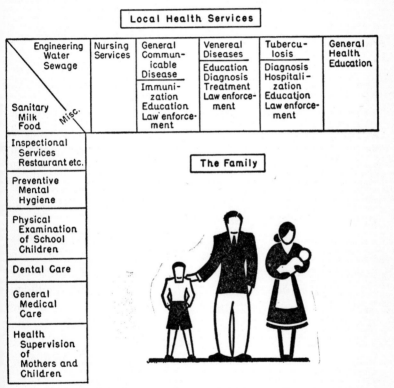

FIGURE 16. Characteristic Methods of Health Administration—Local Agencies Operate Directly. Source: Joseph W. Mountin and Evelyn Flook, *Guide to Health Organization in the United States* (U. S. Public Health Service Miscellaneous Publication No. 35 [Washington, D. C., 1946]), p. ix.

Fig. 16). Although the larger political units have more divisions or departments within the official health organization, the following six are basic:

Statistics	Environmental sanitation
Maternal and child health	Laboratories
Communicable disease control	Public health education

Although all six departments of the official health agency may at times be directly concerned with school health, the services of the departments of communicable disease control, environmental sanitation, and maternal and child health are usually most closely related to the school health program. In addition to his duties with the health department, the director of the department of maternal and child health may also have responsibility for the school health services program. In the larger cities there may be a separate department of school health services within the department of health.

The general activities of the local health department are listed by Mustard:

1. It investigates communicable diseases, including tuberculosis and venereal diseases, and institutes precautions designed to prevent spread of these diseases.
2. It investigates and supervises general sanitary conditions, especially as they relate to the safety of water and the disposal of human excreta.
3. It inspects and supervises the production, pasteurization, and distribution of milk.
4. It supervises the quality and safety of food and meat for public consumption, and attempts to exclude carriers of disease organisms from among the workers in food establishments.
5. It carries on regular inspection to obviate dangers to workers in industrial plants of various sorts.
6. It examines school children for the discovery of communicable diseases or physical defects, notifying parents and school authorities of findings, and urges that the family physician or a clinic be consulted for treatment. In some places school health work is a responsibility of the department of education.
7. It maintains health conferences for expectant mothers, infants, and young children not otherwise under medical supervision.

8. It conducts free clinics for the early diagnosis of tuberculosis, and may conduct mass surveys for discovery of cases.

9. It conducts free clinics for the diagnosis and treatment of venereal diseases in those not able to pay for this care.

10. It conducts clinics for the administration of protective agents: against diphtheria, smallpox, typhoid fever, and sometimes other inoculations.

11. It conducts special clinics: in relation to vision, heart, cancer, mental hygiene, etc., for selected groups.

12. It maintains a public health nursing service, which participates in many activities—in clinics, in schools, in health education—and makes instructive visits in certain cases, thus assisting the family in carrying out the physician's orders or the regulations of the health department.

13. It provides a laboratory service for assistance to any physician, in diagnosis of communicable diseases, including tuberculosis and syphilis.

14. It acts as one part in the vital statistics collection system, and keeps an orderly record of births and deaths.

15. It usually provides, to physicians, free smallpox and typhoid vaccine, diphtheria toxoid, and certain antitoxins, as diphtheria and tetanus antitoxin.

16. It conducts, continuingly, a program of public health education.

17. It occasionally has as responsibilities the conduct of hospitals (particularly isolation hospitals) and the operation of the garbage collection system and inspection of tenements and housing.

18. It investigates complaints and takes action as to health and sanitary conditions.

19. It may have other miscellaneous duties, not necessarily of importance from a public health standpoint, but which have become responsibilities through local custom.[1]

Relationship to Schools

The teacher will bear in mind that certain activities listed above as functions of the local board of health (for example, the health examination of school children and the

[1] Harry S. Mustard, *An Introduction to Public Health* (3d ed.; New York: The Macmillan Co., 1953), p. 52. Used by permission of The Macmillan Company.

school nursing services) are carried on by physicians and nurses in the employ of the board of education in instances where the board of education is responsible for school health service work.

An inspection of the foregoing list shows the teacher which departments of the official health agency are responsible for aspects of child health that are of concern to her. For example, control of childhood communicable disease is a responsibility of the local department of health through its bureau of communicable disease control. Incidentally, the local department of health has legal responsibility for the control of communicable disease. Regardless of whether the board of health or the board of education is in charge of school health services, the teacher is free to discuss any of her problems in childhood communicable disease control with the nurse or the physician assigned to her school.

Guidance that the classroom teacher may need concerning the part she plays in persuading and helping parents to obtain the correction of remediable defects of children may be obtained from the physician or nurse representing the bureau of maternal and child health of the local health department. The local official health department may also wish to make available to the classroom teacher the advisory services of its health educator and its materials for use in health education. When the board of education is responsible for the school health program this assistance to the teacher is usually supplied by health specialists employed by this board.

In some communities in the United States there is little or no local public health service. When this situation exists the classroom teacher may obtain assistance in the form of specific advice about health problems by communicating with the state department of health or the state department of education.

Activities of the Welfare Department

In addition to the official health agency, the official welfare agency of a community is a resource in child health problems. This agency is concerned with family problems of which children's problems are a part. It is common practice to use the term *child health problems* in such a way as to imply that the problem starts and ends with the child himself. Actually, the child's problem is a family problem. Failure to act favorably to recommendations for improving the child's health status or inability to pay for needed health service (the two most common reasons remediable defects of children persist) are family problems. The official welfare agency is prepared to come to the assistance of residents of a community who for various reasons need and qualify for a specialized type of service related to a family health problem. In some instances the need will be for direct medical care which the welfare agency arranges to make available. In others, the type of service furnished aids indirectly in the solution of a health problem. Supplying a housekeeper to keep a family group together while the mother is hospitalized or providing temporary domiciliary care for children are examples of this. Many times, attention to family problems helps to solve the health problem of the school child.

Although the basic purpose of welfare organizations is not the amelioration of individual or community health problems, many health problems are very definitely associated with aspects of living usually considered to lie within the area of responsibility of welfare groups. Problems of sanitary housing and of nutrition as related to the economic ability to obtain adequate food are in the province of both community health and welfare. The growing tendency for a closer working relationship between the health and the welfare groups is evidence of an understanding of the interdependence of these two community services.

Unofficial Community Organizations

The unofficial health agencies came into existence to meet a community health need.

Types of Voluntary Health Agencies

Public health work in the United States is performed by official and unofficial organizations. Much of the pioneering work has been done by the unofficial organizations. A classification of these may be made on the basis of their original purposes—professional, promotional, social foundations, and other types of health services.[2]

The professional organization has a membership made up of specialists in the field of health who, through their organization, desire to further the professional interests of members and to improve their services to the community. The American Medical Association and the National Organization for Public Health Nursing are among the older and better-known organizations in this group.

The promotional organization is concerned with a specific aspect of community health that cannot be or is not being cared for by existing health agencies. These organizations assume responsibility for (1) the control of a specific disease, (2) the preventive work associated with a specific organ, or (3) the constructive work with special community groups. The National Tuberculosis Association, which has a state association in each state and local organizations in the vast majority of communities in the United States, is concerned with the prevention and the control of tuberculosis. The National Society for the Prevention of Blindness, which is concerned with the conservation of vision, and the National Society for Crippled Children and Adults, which is concerned with the social and the vocational rehabilitation of the crippled, are examples of promotional health agencies in the three classifications mentioned above.

[2] Robert G. Paterson, *Foundations of Community Health Education* (New York: McGraw-Hill Book Co., Inc., 1950), p. 203.

Of the many social foundations, the Rockefeller Foundation is well known nationally and internationally for its achievements in the fields of medicine and public health.

Other types of organizations make health services and materials available to communities. Health projects of the American Red Cross and sponsorship of child health programs by the National Congress of Parents and Teachers illustrate the kind of service these organizations provide. In addition, there are numerous commercial organizations which have state or local representatives and which are making excellent contributions to the field of child health. These organizations provide many health education aids to the community.

Services to Schools

Many of the organizations, professional, promotional, social foundations, and other types, make varied health services and materials available to teachers for classroom use.[3]

The kinds of resource the teacher uses are determined by the problems with which she is faced in her classroom activities. A child with whom she works may require medical care, and in some instances, the child's family may need the services of a welfare organization. Her class may have need for health education materials which a voluntary or a commercial health organization can make available. Conceivably, the teacher uses many of the medical welfare and educational services and the materials of unofficial health agencies if these services and materials are readily available to her.

After matters of policy have been settled, the details of working arrangements between schools and community health agencies for obtaining services to schools are usually a responsibility of the school nurse. However, the teacher

[3] See pages 218-19 for a list of organizations from which materials may be obtained.

may, and with the approval of the school administrator does in some instances, assume this responsibility. For example, in many communities in the United States the local tuberculosis association carries on a program of diagnostic testing for school children as part of the broad community program for the prevention of tuberculosis. This work is commonly carried on by the association in cooperation with the school health services department. In situations where a well-organized school health department does not exist the class-room teacher works directly with the tuberculosis association in arranging for this preventive program in the school. Similar arrangements may be made for using the resources of other unofficial health agencies for such services as are required by children handicapped by heart defects, marked vision and hearing defects, psychological-psychiatric problems, or the after-effects of poliomyelitis.

Many of the unofficial health organizations have prepared printed and visual aids material which may be used in school health education. Ordinarily, these have been developed to further an understanding of the particular aspect of community or personal health with which the organization is concerned. They may take the form of units of study constructed for various grade levels or may consist of supplementary material for use with particular topics in the health education program. The health education materials available from such sources are usually good, and the classroom teacher can invariably make effective use of them in her teaching program. In addition some organizations have trained staff members available for consultive work in schools. The teacher may find this type of resource particularly useful as a supplement to her health program. Before the health education materials for classroom use and the services of unofficial health agency staff members are utilized by the teacher, they are approved by the school administrator.

Mention should be made of the fact that such services from unofficial health agencies are not available in many communities. This makes the work of the nurse or the teacher more difficult when she attempts to improve the health status of her school group. Where this situation does exist, health specialists such as physicians and dentists may be counted on for cooperation both as individuals and as members of professional groups. There are many communities where medical and dental practitioners contribute services through their local professional societies to clinics organized to serve low-income and indigent families.

Voluntary Welfare Agency

The unofficial voluntary welfare agency makes available to families essentially the same kind of services as is made available by the official agency, but greater flexibility usually is possible in the acceptance of families making up the case load of the voluntary agency. This is because the regulations that govern the acceptance of cases by the voluntary agency can be modified more easily. In the larger school systems relationships between the school and the unofficial welfare agency are maintained by the guidance, the pupil personnel, or the social service departments of the educational system. In small school systems, responsibility for these relationships is commonly assumed by the classroom teacher.

Parent-Teacher Association

The parent-teacher association is an excellent source of community support for changes in the school health program which are necessary from time to time if this work is to progress. On occasion, the support of this organization has been instrumental in helping to establish and to extend the school program of child health. One of the standing committees of the local parent-teacher association is the school health committee. In addition to sponsoring association meetings devoted to child health problems, this group can be quite effective in making clear the responsibility of parents for the preventive and the remedial care of their children. A school program of nutrition, which requires attention to the eating habits of children as well as to the kind and the amount of food each child eats, is largely dependent on the cooperation of the home for its effectiveness. An active parent-teacher association, which requires the enthusiastic support of principal and teachers as well as parents, can help materially in bringing about the school-home cooperation necessary in this kind of project.

School Health Council

Whether in the form of a community-wide or a school-system council or in the form of a single-school faculty health committee, health councils have the common purpose of giving aid in the solution of health problems by cooperative activity. For example, the ramifications of the problem of dental caries are many. Periodic prophylaxis, caries prevention treatment, reparative work, and extractions are all part of the over-all problem, one which may require the services of the dentist, dental hygienist, school nurse, classroom teacher, and home visitor, if these various professional persons are available. Cooperative activity on the part of each person involved is necessary in order to avoid the overlapping of services and the bewildering of parents, both of which can result from unorganized follow-up work in connection with a remediable defect.

Possibly the most important service rendered by a health council or health committee is the planned approach to the organization of learning experiences for more effective health teaching and to the solution of health problems of individual school pupils. Out of the group experience of planning for the solution of school health problems comes an understanding by the various specialists in the group of the contributions made by others. These council or committee groups representing lay and professional persons—all of whom are fundamentally concerned with the problems of the school child and are organized on a wide community basis or as a single-school committee—can be most helpful to the classroom teacher and can make her contribution to school health more effective.

SELECTED REFERENCES

BURNEY, LEROY E. "Community Organization—An Effective Tool," *American Journal of Public Health*, XLIV (January, 1954), 1-6.

COHEN, ABRAM, D.D.S. "Public Relations—An Integral Part of a School Health Program," *Journal of School Health*, XXIV (June, 1954), 151-60.

HISCOCK, IRA V. (ed.). *Community Health Organization*, 4th ed. New York: Commonwealth Fund, 1950.

KOOS, E. L. "New Concepts in Community Organization for Health," *American Journal of Public Health*, XLIII (April, 1953), 466-69.

MOUNTIN, JOSEPH W., and FLOOK, EVELYN. *Guide to Health Organization in the United States*. (Publication of the U. S. Public Health Service, Miscellaneous Publication No. 35.) Washington, D. C.: Government Printing Office, 1947.

NEW YORK STATE INTER-DEPARTMENTAL HEALTH COUNCIL. *Coordination of School and Community Health Services*. Albany, N. Y.: New York State Department of Health, 1950.

PATERSON, ROBERT G. *Foundations of Community Health Education*. New York: McGraw-Hill Book Co., Inc., 1950.

UNDERWOOD, FELIX J., M.D. "Departments of Education and Public Health Working Together," *American Journal of Public Health*, XLIV (May, 1954), 625-30.

Chapter 12

EVALUATION OF THE SCHOOL HEALTH PROGRAM

THE SOLE purpose of school programs in health is to maintain and to improve the health of the individual school child. Each child inherits certain biological tendencies to grow and to develop in accordance with a pattern of his own. Unless this pattern is changed he progresses toward maturity in an orderly fashion. Through preventive, corrective, and educational procedures, a sound school health program helps to prevent interference with this orderly pattern of growth and development. Influences which are detrimental to the child are avoided, such as accidents, the effects of certain childhood diseases, disturbed emotional states, and faulty nutrition arising from inadequate amounts and kinds of food. Within the limits of established policy the soundly conceived school health program arranges to supply every kind of service that contributes directly or indirectly to the health welfare of each pupil.

The competent teacher and administrator do not indulge in the assumption that their existing practices in school health services, in health instruction, and in environmental conditions are effective. Evaluation of these various aspects of the school health program is the only way in which effectiveness can be determined. Such a procedure determines whether existing practices are actually effective to the point of assuring each child optimum growth and development as he progresses toward maturity.

Procedures for Evaluation

The teacher (or administrator or health specialist) who is interested in evaluation proceeds in accordance with a logical plan. She will—

1. Decide the specific outcomes for each objective of the program.
2. Determine the measuring instruments which she wishes to use.
3. Analyze and interpret the results of measurement.
4. Make application of the findings for improvement of the program.

Instruments of Measurement

Listed below are some of the commonly used instruments which the teacher may find useful in evaluation procedures.

1. Health record card, which provides information about the pupil as it is obtained through the services of school health specialists.
2. Health tests, either oral or written, which enable the teacher to gain accurate information about the pupil's health knowledge (see Chap. 8).
3. Observations of the behavior of a pupil when he acts in situations which involve health choices such as obtaining first-aid care for minor abrasions or wearing clothing appropriate for the weather.
4. Appraisal of the related interests of pupils, such as work in art or special school activities, which indicate concepts of health.
5. Checklists which are devised to obtain information about the health behavior of pupils or to find out about their interests in specific topics that relate to child health (see Chap. 8).

6. Surveys which are designed to obtain information about specific health conditions of pupils or about the effectiveness of certain procedures in the school health program. The survey of the eating habits of children which was referred to previously gives general information about nutritional status. When a survey is employed, it is necessary to use standards that are related to the item surveyed.

7. Questionnaires which are used by the nurse or the teacher and are designed to furnish information about the reaction of parents and others in the community to various parts of the program, such as their understanding of the purpose of the health appraisal.

8. Reports which give information about the consumption in school of protective foods, or about changes in environmental conditions, for example.

Types of Evaluation

Evaluation of various kinds and in varying degrees goes on continually in the school. The process consists of using techniques which are designed to indicate the extent to which existing practices accomplish the purpose for which they are intended. That is, do the outcomes of a program indicate that the stated aims of the program have been achieved. In connection with the school health program there are two types of evaluation:

1. The first type compares with recognized standards the procedures used to attain the objectives of the school health program. Included are all aspects of the health services program, environmental conditions, and health instruction. The specific activities of school personnel engaged in health work and the methods they use in their work are included. Measures of the relationship between the school and other community agencies are also important. In short, every part of the school health program is matched against standards for that part of the program.

2. The other type assesses the individual at the beginning and at the end of his participation in some aspect of the school health program by—

   a) Determining health status as this is indicated by cumulative health appraisal reports.

   b) Determining changes in status as shown by progress in the development of desirable habits, understandings, and attitudes.

Comparison with Accepted Standards

The following illustrate how recognized good practices (standards) may be used as a basis for evaluation:

Cooperation in the health services program. The educational aspects of such health service work as immunizing treatment (if this is given through the schools) and preliminary educational work associated with tuberculosis prevention programs are recognized as a responsibility of the school and require the support of the administrator and the staff if they are to be effective.

The school administrator and his staff give all necessary cooperation in arrangements which require the use of school facilities for clinical work, regardless of whether the work is done by the school health department or by the local department of health.

Standards in healthful school living. The environmental conditions under which teacher and pupil work, classroom lighting and hand-washing facilities for example, may be evaluated. They indicate, to a certain extent, the attitude of school personnel toward factors which are basic to a good health program.

The teacher has practically complete control over classroom conditions as they relate to pupil-teacher and pupil-to-pupil relationships. By her own attitudes and behavior, she establishes the pleasant, harmonious working relationships which are necessary for a high order of learning. The standards which were suggested in Chapter 10 may be used by the classroom teacher as a basis for matching her classroom practices against desirable practices.

Administrative recognition for the school health program. The allocation of a specific time allotment for health instruction in the upper elementary grades is one of the important requirements for an effective school health program.

Planning a curriculum that relates health teaching to other school activities and providing teaching aids in health indicate good practices in school organization for health instruction.

Relationships between the classroom teacher and special health personnel should be as direct as good administrative technique permits. That is, the teacher has direct access to the opinion of physicians, dentists, and other health specialists when she needs advice about a pupil or guidance in any health problem.

Characteristic of a school that ranks high in an evaluation of its health program are provisions for in-service education in health through staff meetings, careful delineation of responsibilities that involve both the health specialists and the classroom teacher, and establishment and active support of a school health council.

Effective school-community relationships. The area of school-home relationships offers an intangible but important source of information for use in evaluation. Evidence which indicates the effectiveness of principal, teacher, and nurse in community relationships does not lend itself to precise measurement, but may be obtained by utilizing critical incidents or an accumulation of incidents that result from contacts between school staff and parents. Within limits prescribed by economic considerations, the extent to which the home takes responsibility for, and carries out, the recommendations of the classroom teacher or the school health staff for the correction of remediable defects or for attention to the nutritional needs of a child is an indication of whether good school-home relationships have been achieved. The willingness of the home or its failure to cooperate with the teacher or the nurse in child health matters is unmistakable evidence of the effectiveness of school staff members in this important aspect of school health work.

Beyond the confines of the school, effective working relationships should be established and maintained with community health agencies. The services and the educational resources of the official and voluntary health agencies are utilized whenever a contribution by these agencies can be made to the school's program in health.

An awareness that teamwork by the school and the home is a necessary condition for accomplishment in child health work means that parent-teacher association activities are encouraged and supported by the school administrator and his staff.

Assessment of the Individual

Assessing the individual requires a number of different approaches and a corresponding number of different techniques. Through health services a sound school health program affects desirably the distinctly biological characteristics of the pupil. The climate of the classroom in which he spends the greater part of the school day has an effect on his emotional development and on his attitudes. The instructional program should influence his attitudes toward health matters, and through the acquisition of an understanding of them, enables him to choose well. In measuring the extent of these potentially desirable influences on the child the correct instrument must be used, and in this connection, it is timely to point out that evidence of improvement in pupil status is not always the consequence of school experiences exclusively. The influence of commercial advertising may be a persuasive factor. However, it is not unreasonable to assume a direct relationship between improved status in the majority of a group and the fact that they have taken part in a program designed to accomplish such improvement. In any evaluation there is need for the measuring instrument to measure, with reasonable accuracy, the thing it purports to measure.

Certain information about pupils comes from such measuring instruments as the cumulative health record card. Among other items this card carries the record of repeated judgments of the physician in his clinical appraisal of the pupil. The physician's subjective judgment provides a general basis for determining the child's status; he then may be compared nutritionally with other children, or still better, with his own previous record. The health history reveals whether the child has received protection through immunization treatments. It also shows the progress in the correction of remediable defects, vision and hearing for example. The record of physical growth and development gives evidence of the extent to which the individual child is meeting a desirable standard. These measurements of change, which give a basis for evaluation, are direct and relatively easy to obtain. Some are quantitative, as physical measurements of height and weight for example, and in the evaluative procedure are capable of direct comparison with previous measurements of the child.

The health behavior of the child, which is determined partly by her own observation and partly by reports, indicates to the teacher the effectiveness of the school experiences which were designed to improve this health behavior. Evidence of change in health habits, understandings, and attitudes may be determined, in some instances, through direct observation, but in other instances, evidence of change must be determined by indirect means. For example, a desirable change in the habit of hand-washing prior to eating may, if done without recourse to teacher insistence, be considered evidence that previous health education experiences designed to produce such an end-result have been successful. The observation (instrument for measuring) results in a direct measure of changed behavior. On the other hand, evidence through a health knowledge test that an individual understands both the beneficial and the undesirable consequences of a certain course of action which involves health behavior indicates that he is equipped, as far as knowledge is concerned, to make a right choice in reference to a specific health problem. Presumably, the test (instrument for measuring) gives evidence of improvement in health knowledge. The measurement is indirect in that the potential for correct health behavior is being measured and not the behavior itself.

It is possible to infer the kind and the extent of a pupil's understandings by taking notice of his comments and observing his actions with respect to his needs. Findley and Scates state, as follows:

As a matter of fact, some understandings are best assessed when they are assessed informally. Written tests and other formal instruments or appraisal make their unique contributions, but frequently the best evidence of a pupil's understanding is reflected in reactions that may escape the teacher's notice. There are, for example, many personal meanings, sensitivities, appreciations, and values (all involving understanding) which are closely guarded by pupils and which will not be revealed except when some situation engrosses them so completely that they forget themselves. The ordinary school day affords many such situations, and the occasions thus made available for observing significant behavior should be utilized to the full.[1]

[1] Warren G. Findley and Douglas E. Scates, "Obtaining Evidence of Understanding," in *The Measurement of Understanding*, Forty-fifth Yearbook of the National Society for the Study of Education, Part I (Chicago: University of Chicago Press, 1946), p. 45.

The classroom teacher is usually not concerned with giving tests designed to determine the attitude of pupils toward health matters, but she is able to determine by observation whether the attitude of a child toward items of personal health behavior is desirable. She is aware that the child's predisposition to react in a definite manner to matters of personal health is an indication of his attitude (see Chap. 8). In the development of attitudes, the home and the community are basically influential. Nevertheless, opportunities occur in the school program for the development in the child of desirable attitudes toward health matters. The teacher thus has another means of evaluating the effectiveness of her health program by observing the child's improvement in these attitudes.

SELECTED REFERENCES

GATES, ARTHUR I., and STRANG, RUTH M. *Gates-Strang Health Knowledge Test,* rev. ed. New York: Bureau of Publications, Teachers College, Columbia University, 1945.

GROUT, RUTH E. *Health Teaching in Schools,* 2d ed. Philadelphia: W. B. Saunders Co., 1953, pp. 257-72.

METROPOLITAN LIFE INSURANCE COMPANY. *The School Health Program.* (School Health Monograph No. 12.) New York: The Company, 1950.

OBERTEUFFER, DELBERT. *School Health Education,* rev. ed. New York: Harper & Bros., 1954, pp. 202-22.

PATTY, WILLARD W. "Preliminary Construction Principles Relating to Health Education Tests," *Journal of School Health,* XX (October, 1950), 226-31.

SMILEY, DEAN F., and HEIN, FRED V. (eds.). *Health Appraisal of School Children.* Report of the Joint Committee on Health Problems in Education of the National Education Association and the American Medical Association. Washington, D. C.: National Education Association, and Chicago: American Medical Association, 1948.

WEATHERBE, HAROLD R. *A Check List for School Health Services.* Stanford, Calif.: Stanford University Press, 1952.

WILSON, CHARLES C. (ed.). *Health Education,* 4th ed. Washington, D. C.: National Education Association, 1948, pp. 337-50.

———(ed.). *School Health Services.* Report of the Joint Committee on Health Problems in Education of the National Education Association and the American Medical Association. Washington, D. C.: National Education Association, and Chicago: American Medical Association, 1953, pp. 399-413.

YANKAUER, ALFRED, M.D. "Designs for Evaluation Needed in the School Health Services Field," *American Journal of Public Health*, XLII (June, 1952), 655-60.

GLOSSARY

ABRASION	A place where the skin is rubbed off.
ACUITY	The degree of ability to see or to hear.
ANTIBODY	Any of various substances in the blood which act in antagonism to harmful foreign bodies, such as toxins or bacteria which produce toxins.
ANTIGEN	A substance which when introduced into the body causes the formation of antibodies.
ANTITOXIN	Antibodies which tend to destroy or neutralize toxins.
AUDIOGRAM	A graphic record of a hearing test.
BACILLUS	Straight, rod-shaped bacterium.
BACTERIA	Microscopic organisms including those causing disease.
BINOCULAR VISION	Ability of the individual to fuse the images received by the two eyes into a single scene with the quality of depth.
CARBOHYDRATE	Any food element that is sugar or can be converted into sugar.
CARIES	Decay of teeth.
CARRIERS	Immune persons who harbor germs and unknowingly spread disease.
COMMUNICABLE DISEASE	A disease that may be spread from person to person.
CORNEA	The clear, curved portion of the very front and center of the eye, covering the iris and pupil.
DIAGNOSTICIAN	One who establishes the nature of a case of illness.
EUGENICS	The science treating of the development and improvement of the human race.

FAULTY ARTICULATION	Imperfect enunciation of words.
FILTRABLE VIRUS	A virus that can pass through the pores of a very fine filter.
FLUORINE	An element of the chlorine family, in minute quantities beneficial against tooth decay in children.
FUNGUS	Spore-forming plants that include mushrooms, puffballs, yeasts, blights, smuts, rust, rots, and molds.
FUSION	A blending together. (*See* Binocular vision.)
GLANDS OF INTERNAL SECRETION	Glands which deliver their secretion directly into the bloodstream.
HEMOLYTIC	An agent causing hemolysis (the breaking up of the red blood corpuscles).
HOOKWORM	A species of intestinal worms.
IMMUNITY	The condition in which the organism is secure against any particular disease.
IMMUNIZATION	The process of making a person resistant to a certain disease.
INFESTATION	Invasion of the body by parasites.
ITCH MITE	An insect which burrows into the skin.
METABOLIC RATE	The rate of metabolism as measured by the individual's production of heat.
METABOLISM	Chemical and physical changes of the organism.
MICRO-ORGANISM	A minute living body
MIGRAINE	Severe headache, usually affecting one side of the head.
MORBIDITY RATE	The incidence or amount of sickness.
MORTALITY RATE	The death rate.
OPTICAL SYSTEM	A group of organs which especially contributes toward the function of vision.
PATHOGENIC	Causing disease.
PEDIATRICS	Branch of medicine dealing with the health and diseases of children.
PERCENTILE POSITION	Essentially the rank that one would have in a group of 100.

PHYSIOLOGIC	Concerning normal or healthy functioning.
PLUS SPHERE LENSES	Lenses used to detect hyperopia (farsightedness).
PROPHYLAXIS	The prevention of disease.
PSYCHIATRIST	A physician who treats mental disorders.
REFRACTION	Focusing of rays of light by the eye.
RETINA	The membrane at the back of the eyeball receiving rays of light from object being viewed by the eye.
SPORE	Any germ or reproductive element less organized than a true cell.
STAPHYLOCOCCUS	Round bacteria which arrange themselves in clusters.
STREPTOCOCCUS	Round bacteria arranged in strings.
SUBCUTANEOUS	Beneath the skin.
TITER	A standard of fineness or strength.
TOXINS	Poisonous substances given off by bacteria.
TOXOID	A toxin treated so that it no longer produces tissue damage but stimulates the tissues to produce antitoxin.
TUBERCULIN TEST	The test with a substance derived from the tubercle bacillus, used to determine whether the individual has ever been infected with tuberculosis.
ULTRAVIOLET LIGHT	The rays just beyond the violet end of the visible spectrum.
VACCINE	Any substance for inoculation to prevent disease.
VALIDITY	The extent to which the device actually does what it purports to do.
VIRULENCE	The strength or poisonousness.
VIRUS	An agent smaller than bacteria, capable of self-propagation, which can cause disease.

SOURCE LIST FOR MATERIAL ON CHILD HEALTH

Instructional material and information about child health problems may be obtained from the organizations listed below.

Professional Associations

American Academy of Pediatrics, 636 Church St., Evanston, Ill.
American Association for Health, Physical Education and Recreation, 1201 Sixteenth St., N.W., Washington, D. C.
American Dental Association, 222 East Superior St., Chicago
American Home Economics Association, Mills Building, Seventeenth St. and Pennsylvania Ave., Washington, D. C.
American Hospital Association, 18 East Division St., Chicago
American Medical Association, 535 North Dearborn St., Chicago
American Nurses Association, 1790 Broadway, New York
American Public Health Association, 1790 Broadway, New York
American School Health Association, Urbana, Ill.
Association for Childhood Education, 1200 Fifteenth St., Washington, D. C.
Child Study Association of America, 221 West 57th St., New York
National Association for Nursery Education, Roosevelt College of Chicago, Chicago
National Education Association, 1201 Sixteenth St., N.W., Washington, D. C.
National Organization for Public Health Nursing, 1790 Broadway, New York

U. S. Government

U. S. Children's Bureau, Department of Health, Education, and Welfare, Washington, D. C.
U. S. Department of Agriculture, Washington, D. C.
U. S. Office of Education, Department of Health, Education and Welfare, Washington, D. C.
U. S. Public Health Service, Department of Health, Education, and Welfare, Washington, D. C.

Voluntary Health Organizations

American Cancer Society, 47 Beaver St., New York
American Epilepsy League, Inc., 130 N. Wells St., Chicago
American Hearing Society, 1537 Thirty-fifth St. N.W., Washington, D. C.
American Heart Association, 1790 Broadway, New York
American Red Cross, Seventeenth and D Sts., Washington, D. C.
American Social Hygiene Association, 1790 Broadway, New York
Child Welfare League of America, 130 East 22d St., New York
National Committee for Mental Hygiene, 1790 Broadway, New York

National Foundation for Infantile Paralysis, 120 Broadway, New York
National Safety Council, 20 N. Wacker Drive, Chicago
National Society for Crippled Children and Adults, 10 LaSalle St., Chicago
National Society for the Prevention of Blindness, 1790 Broadway, New York
National Tuberculosis Association, 1790 Broadway, New York

NOTE: Addresses are as of January, 1955.

INDEX

Absences from school, chief cause
    of, 124-25
Accidents
    among children, 146-48
    environmental factors in, 149, 152
    by grade level, 149
    human factors in, 153-55
    immediate causes of, 152
    location of, 148-49
    by type, 149
Accident-susceptibles, 153
Adjustment in mental health, 183-84
American Academy of Pediatrics, on
    factors in prevention and cura-
    tive care, 10
American Association of School Ad-
    ministrators, position on emo-
    tionally disturbed teacher, 190
American Heart Association
    opinion on causes and prevention
        of rheumatic fever, 101
    therapeutic classification of pa-
        tients, 100
American Medical Association, rec-
    ommendations on health exami-
    nations, 35
American Red Cross, health projects
    of, 199
"Areas of health," child interest in,
    130-31
Assessment of the child
    attitudes of pupil, 212
    cumulative record card, 210
    in evaluation, 209-12
    health behavior of pupil, 210-11
    health knowledge test, 211
    procedures in, 14-26
    understandings of pupil, 211
    value for health guidance, 26-27
Astigmatism, 49, 51
Attitudes
    definition of, 118
    in evaluation, 212
    formation of, 118-19
Audiometer; see Phonograph audi-
    ometer, Pure-tone audiometer

Binocular vision, 51
Board of Directors of the Commis-
    sion on Chronic Illness, on
    fluoridation, 112
Board of education
    responsibility for child health, 5
        for school health services, 31-32
Board of health, 192-96
    basic divisions of, 193-94
    chief medical officer, 4
    general activities of, 194-95
    relationship to schools, 195-96
        to welfare department, 197
    responsibility for child health, 3
        for control of communicable
            disease, 4, 77-79, 196
        for school health services, 32
Body measurements
    record form for, 16
    use of, 16, 17
    value of, 16
    by whom determined, 17

Caries prevention
    importance of diet in, 112
    topical application in, 113-14
    use of fluorides in, 112-14
Center for Safety Education, New
    York University, list of immedi-
    ate causes of accidents, 152
"Chain of infection," 67-68
Charts of communicable disease, 70-
    71
Chickenpox, 72
Child behavior; see Mental health
Child welfare, 197, 201-2
Classroom lighting, suggestions for,
    54-55
Classroom teacher
    responsibility for communicable
        disease control, 75-77
        health appraisal, 37
    role in mental health, 181-91
        in physical education program,
            169